Selected from over 1,000 manipulative activities
previously published in *Centers Galore*

HANDS-ON MATH

Editors:
Becky Andrews
Lynn Coble

Artists:
Pam Crane
Susan Hodnett
Becky Saunders
Barry Slate
Jennifer Tipton

Cover Design:
Pam Crane

S0-BFA-589

Table Of Contents

About This Book

Each year from 1980 to 1990, The Education Center's staff and free-lance writers developed a new collection of learning centers to be featured at workshops and presented in our yearly publication, *Centers Galore.* In this book, you'll find the best math manipulative centers selected from the hundreds created by our editors and writers.

These centers can be made from inexpensive materials and adapted to a variety of basic skills. Each idea is pictured in detail, with construction tips and skill information. We've also included suggestions for variations so that you may adapt almost any center to your students' grade level and needs. You'll also find ready-to-use patterns for many of the center pieces and game cards. These patterns can be found on the same page as the center illustration or in the back of the book on pages 176–192.

Five types of centers are featured:

Cut-outs: Poster board cut out in shapes that teach or reinforce a basic skill.

Pocket Pals: Learning activities created on string-tie envelopes that include a playing surface and storage all in one.

Clip-ons: Appealing centers with matching clip-on pieces.

File Folders: Activities to copy on easy-to-store file folders.

Skillboards: Poster-sized (17" x 22") activities suitable for a bulletin board or tabletop.

All of the centers in each category are listed on the first page of that section of the book, along with suggestions for how to make and use the centers in your classroom. Resource pages begin on page 163. Pick a format you like and program a center with a skill you want to stress.

Cut-outs

We suggest making our Cut-outs on 17" x 22" sheets of poster board. They can be used for a bulletin board; can be placed on the blackboard, the door, or the floor; or can be used as a teaching aid when you are working with a small group.

Because most of the figures are universal in their appeal and can be used during any season, plan to make your centers reusable. Make parts changeable by attaching them with rubber cement, brads, paper clips, magnetic tape, or Velcro.

Tick Tock Tabby

Students will be eager to set the time on Tabby's clock. After completing the artwork, laminate and cut out the center and clock hands. Attach the hands to the clock with a brad. Copy the blank clock cards on page 163. On each clock, draw hands to show a specific time; then mount the cards on tagboard, laminate, and cut out. With a permanent marker, program the backs of the cards with times that match the clocks. (Students will check themselves with the clock faces.) Store the cards in a pocket on the back of the center.

Draw a card from the pocket on the back. Show the time on this clock. To check, turn the card over.

Jeepers Peepers!

Where'd you get those eyes? Attach spinners with brads to this gentleman for plenty of addition facts practice. After students have worked with these numbers for several days, clip new directions over the old ones, instructing students to spin and subtract the smaller number from the larger.

Provide your students with creative story starters by reprogramming the wheels with settings and characters.

Spin two numbers.
Add to find their sum.

Paper Boys

Extra! Extra! Here's a center that's just right for practicing the concept of greater than/less than. Attach paper pockets to the center as shown. Duplicate the newspaper cards on page 176 on construction paper. Label the cards with number comparison sentences, omitting the > and < signs. Laminate the cards, if desired, and cut them apart. To make the activity self-checking, write the correct sign on the back of each card.

To get more use from this center, apply new pockets and label additional cards with facts/opinions, correct/incorrect math problems, or odd/even numbers.

Watermelon Wingding

Try the "poke-and-peek" format on an interesting cut-out shape, such as the watermelon slice shown here. After writing subtraction problems on the front of the center, punch holes as indicated. Turn the center over and write a matching answer on the back beside each hole. Provide a plastic drinking straw for students to poke in the holes.

Use this deliciously fun center to take a bite out of other skills: addition facts, *r*-controlled vowels, and homonyms.

Spare Change

Use the reproducible coin cards on pages 165–167 to make this center. Duplicate the cards; then laminate and cut them apart. Store the cards in a pocket on the back of the center. Label a set of blank cards with various tasks such as the one shown in the illustration. Store these cards in the pocket as well. A student removes the cards from the pocket, chooses one task card, then places the correct coin cards on the purse to fulfill the task card directions. Program the back of each task card so students can check their answers.

Adapt this giant purse for practicing categorization, fact families, or rhyming words.

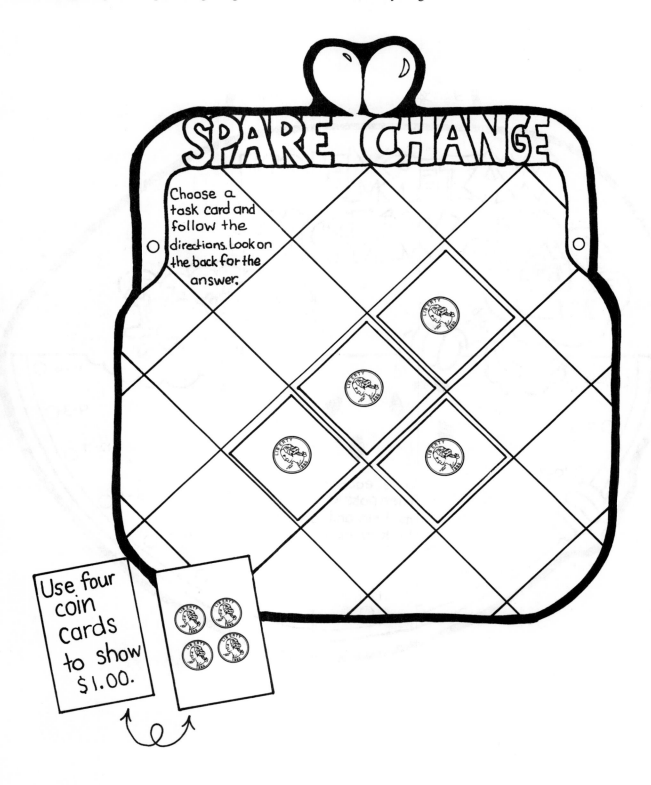

©1991 **The Education Center, Inc.**

Calico Cat

This patchwork kitty needs help finding her patches! Provide practice with shape recognition by cutting geometric patches from **different colors** and types of paper. Store the cutouts in a pocket attached to the back of the center.

Place each patch on the right space.

Calico Cat

A Show Of Hands

Hands up for numeration drill! Trace and cut out ten paper mittens using the pattern on page 176. Draw a dot set on **each mitten** to match a number on the center (or use the reproducible dot sets on page 171). Attach a pocket to the back of the center to **store the** mittens.

For a change, glue cut-out pictures on the mittens and write initial or final consonants on the hands. Or program the **mittens with** uppercase letters to match to lowercase letters on the hands.

Place each mitten on the correct hand.

3 5 9

7 4 1

2 8

10 6

A Show of Hands

Straight From The Horse's Mouth

Here's a filly with an appetite for fractions! Cut a slit at the top of the horse's feed bucket; then attach a paper pocket on the back of the center directly below the slit. Label a set of cards with correctly and incorrectly labeled fraction pictures (see sample cards below). Store the cards in the bucket's slit.

Use this open format with other skills as well: math facts, states/capitals, punctuation, spelling.

Monster Grip

This damsel in distress needs a hero who knows his multiplication facts! Enlarge the damsel pattern on page 176 on construction paper; then glue it to a piece of tagboard and cut it out again. Label the damsel with answers to the problems on the center. After a student writes the answers on his paper, he pulls up the answer strip to check his work. Mount a piece of paper behind the center to secure the answer strip.

If you wish to use Monster Grip to practice language arts skills, label the center with homonyms, singular nouns to write as plural nouns, or word pairs to write as contractions. Make and program a new answer strip.

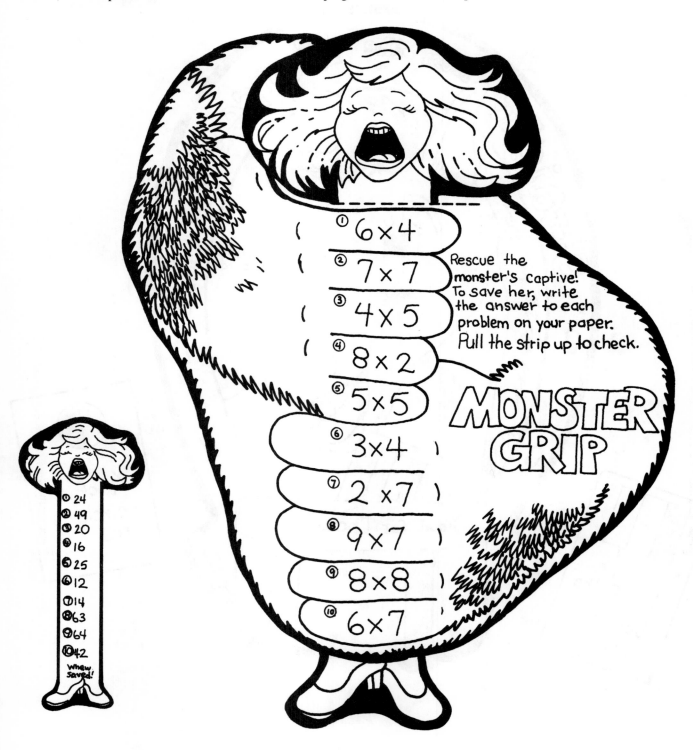

©1991 The Education Center, Inc.

Sugar Shack

Sweeten counting practice with an ice-cream cone that's fun to put together. Attach a spinner to the center of the number wheel. Use the patterns on page 177 to cut out scoops of ice cream from various colors and textures of paper. Store the scoops in a pocket attached to the back of the center.

To adapt this sweet center for language arts, label the wheel with short and long vowels. Write words on the cut-out scoops. A student spins the spinner; then she finds the correct scoops to add to the cone.

Coffee Break

All you need to complete this "poke-and-peek" center is a plastic drinking straw. After labeling the center with division problems, punch holes as indicated. On the back of the center, write a matching answer beside each hole.

For a change, draw trail game spaces around the perimeter of the mug. Write new directions on the center. Provide a stack of skill cards, markers, a die, and an answer key.

Give each answer.
To check, poke a straw through the hole and look on the back

○ 45÷9
○ 16÷4
○ 27÷3
○ 25÷5
○ 72÷8
○ 54÷9

36÷6 ○
30÷5 ○
54÷6 ○
18÷2 ○
81÷9 ○
21÷7 ○

15÷3 ○   56÷8 ○   64÷8 ○

Cut-outs

Greta Ghost

This "boo-tiful" little ghost is grinning from ear to ear about the place value practice she provides. Cut two slits on Greta where indicated. Program a tagboard strip as shown. Insert the strip in Greta's two slits. The student reads the number in the "window," names the place value of the underlined digit, then pulls the strip down to check.

Program additional strips to practice math facts, vowels, or spelling words.

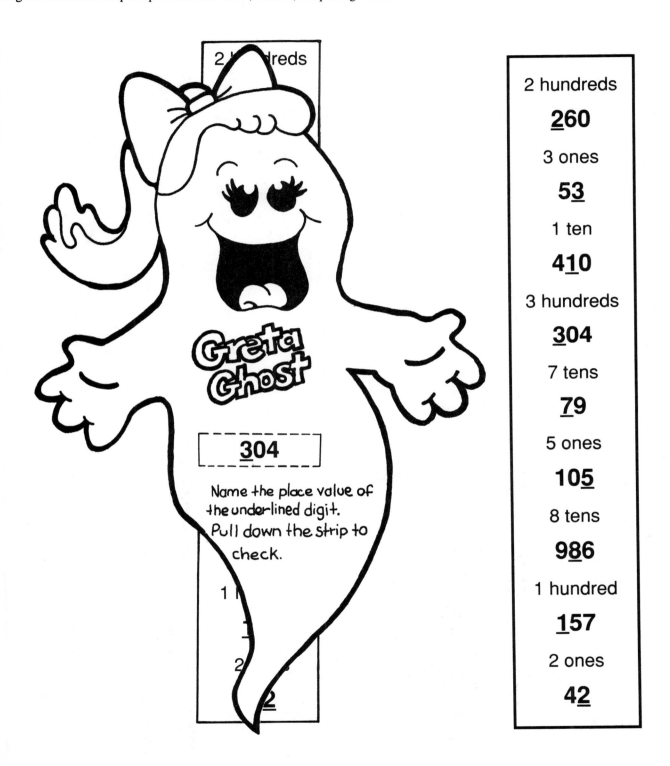

2 hundreds

2_60

3 ones

5_3

1 ten

4_1_0

3 hundreds

_3_04

7 tens

_7_9

5 ones

10_5_

8 tens

9_8_6

1 hundred

_1_57

2 ones

4_2_

©1991 The Education Center, Inc.

17

Stars And Stripes

Your students will surely salute this patriotic math center. Using the star patterns on page 177, duplicate nine stars on red construction paper. Duplicate seven more star patterns on blue construction paper. Cut out the stars; then use a marker to add stripes to the nine red stars. Attach a pocket to the back of the center to store the star cutouts.

To vary the skill, write hard-*g*/soft-*g* words on the center. Have students cover the hard-*g* words with the striped stars and the soft-*g* words with the plain stars. Change the center's directions.

STARS And STRIPES

Put a striped star on each odd number.
Put a plain star on each even number.

31   10   53

17   68   81   6

5   75   43

23   12

50   9

38   24

The Big Cheese

This mouse is busy nibbling away at addition problems! Cut the cheese circle and the mouse (pattern on page 177) out of poster board; then fasten them together with a brad. Instruct the student to solve the problems on his paper. Store an answer key in a pocket attached to the back of the center.

To change the problems easily, laminate the center before programming it. When you're ready for a change, wipe the center clean and reprogram it using a wipe-off marker.

Cannonball Jones

Send Cannonball into orbit while counting by 5s! Enlarge the pattern of Cannonball on page 178. After coloring and cutting out the pattern, cut along the dotted line around Cannonball's arm. Program the strip with missing-number sequences as shown. Insert Cannonball in a slit on the cut-out. The student pulls up the strip to reveal one problem at a time.

For a change, use Cannonball to practice sight words, plurals, or abbreviations.

Tunin' In

Tune in sequencing practice at this cool center! Cut out sets of eight notes each (see the note patterns on page 178). Write numbers to sequence on each set. Cut eight slits in the Cut-out and insert a paper clip in each as shown.

For variety, make additional note sets labeled with letters of the alphabet, days of the week, months of the year, or words to alphabetize.

Shopping Spree!

Make use of actual grocery ads from the newspaper for some true-to-life money practice. Cut a slit on the shopping cart where shown and insert a paper clip. Clip a newspaper ad (or one that you've written) to the center. Label a set of cards with brief shopping lists. Store them in a pocket on the center. The student chooses one card from the pocket and adds to find the total.

For more advanced students, provide task cards that require subtraction as well as addition.

Bookworm At Work!

You'll get plenty of mileage from this studious crawler! Cut slits as shown on the book. Use the pattern to make several bookworm strips, each the width of the slits (or slightly smaller). Label each strip with numbers for students to read. Insert a strip into the book's slits as shown.

Label additional bookworm strips with vocabulary or sight words, math facts, or letters to identify.

15
4
3
12
7
10
6
8
1
14
2
5
9
11
13

Pattern

Say the number.

Push the bookworm up.

Time To Practice

When it's time to practice time-telling skills, let this friendly ape lead the way! Cut slits along the dotted lines and insert paper clips. Label paper circles with times. To make matching clock face circles, duplicate the cards on page 163. Then add hands to each clock before cutting it out. Store the circles and the cut-out clocks in a pocket attached to the back of the center.

This center is also ideal for matching upper-/lowercase letters and numbers/sets.

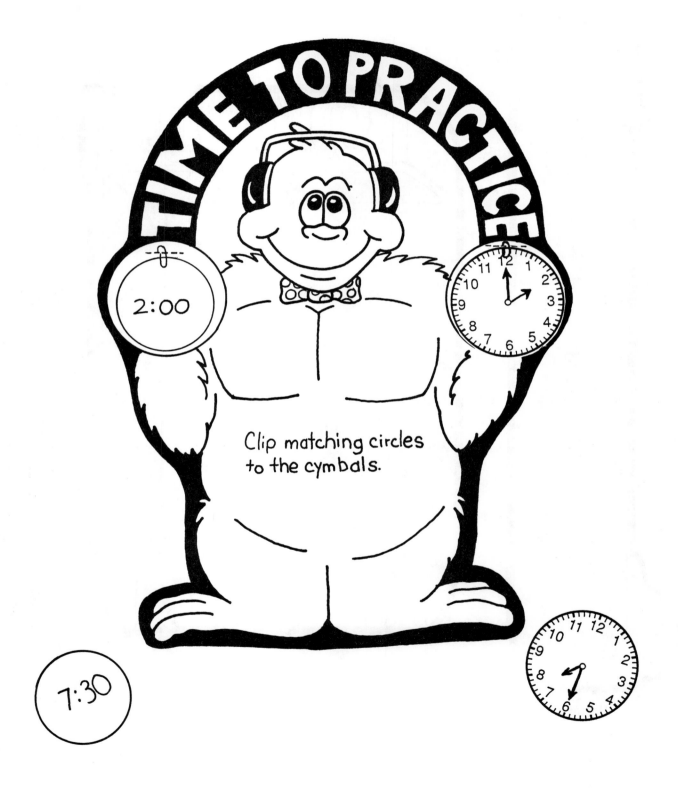

The Terrible Two

Interchangeable, tachistoscope strips make this center versatile. Make slits where indicated by the dotted lines. Cut out a strip of poster board, insert it as shown, and write in math problems. Remove the strip, turn it over, and reinsert. Write in the matching answers. (Notice that answer #7 ends up in back of problem #1.)

Make extra strips and label with more math problems, contractions, or abbreviations.

Love Potion #9

Your students will love calculating addition answers with a dose of Love Potion #9. Use the heart patterns on page 178 to make 15 construction paper hearts. Label nine hearts with correctly solved problems. Label the remaining hearts with incorrect problems. Store the hearts in a pocket on the front of the Cut-out. The student takes a heart from the pocket, solves the problem on her paper, and places the heart on the correct beaker. If she has placed the hearts correctly, she will have nine hearts on the Powerful Potions beaker.

Adapt this center to other sorting skills: incomplete/complete sentences, hard-/soft-*g* words, upper-/lowercase letters.

Help Dr. Kiss find nine love potions that work! Solve each problem on the hearts. If the problem is correct, place it on the Powerful Potions beaker. If it's incorrect, place it on the Fizzled Formulas beaker. When you're finished, you should have nine Powerful Potions hearts.

Warm Wishes

Use this open activity all year long! Cut out a stack of cards to fit the quilt squares, and label with subtraction or other math facts. Store the cards and an answer key in a pocket on the front of the center.

Make additional sets of cards labeled with missing-vowel words, numbers to round, or word pairs to write as contractions. Provide answer keys.

Solve each problem.
Check the key.
If correct, turn the patch over
    and place it on the quilt.
Can you cover the quilt
    with patches?

Crow's Nest

This spyglass grows and grows as your students place numbered cutouts in the correct order. Use the pattern to make a set of spyglass pieces. Label them with numbers to sequence. Store the pieces and the end piece of the spyglass in a pocket attached to the back of the center.

Label additional cutouts with story events, or words or letters to alphabetize.

CROW'S NEST

Make the spyglass by putting the cards in order.

Pattern

Busy Beaver

Get busy on improving addition skills with the help of this toothy friend. Attach a spinner to the wheel. Cut two small slits in the **beaver's hat**; then insert a strip labeled with a number. Change the number strip in the beaver's hat frequently for lots of varied practice. For older children, change the directions and have students multiply by the number on the beaver's hat.

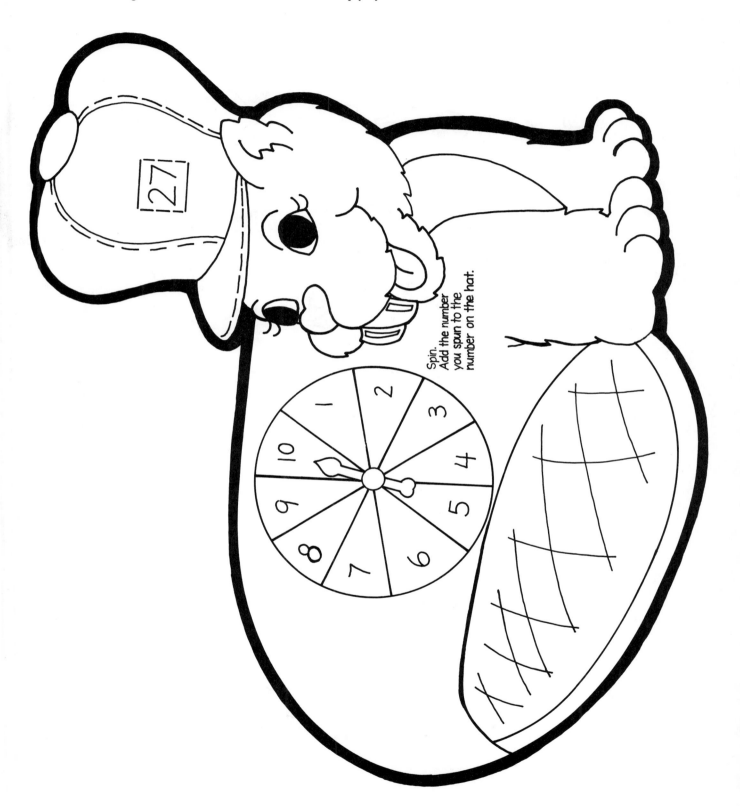

Spin.
Add the number
you spun to the
number on the hat.

Balancing Buddies

Use this center to help students learn to count money. Draw the seals with their fish and laminate. Cut slits for paper clips on the fish. On one set of fish cards (see the patterns on page 179), stamp coins (or use the reproducible coins on pages 165–167). Label a matching set of cards with corresponding amounts. Store the cards in a pocket on the back of the Cut-out.

Make other sets of cards labeled with rhyming words, contractions/word pairs, or math facts/answers.

Find the matching cards. Clip them to the fish.

Bubble Blow-up

A spinner makes this counting center fun for beginning students. After completing the artwork, laminate; then attach a spinner to the number wheel. Tape a pocket to the front of the center to store ten bubble cutouts.

For a more difficult activity, label the wheel with fractions and provide matching picture bubbles.

Wacky Walkathon

Be a winner in the wacky math walkathon! Cut a slit along the dotted line and insert a paper clip. Label a cut-out card with a math operation and number. Students spin the spinner and follow the directions on the card.

Quackers And Milk

Students may get "all 'quacked' up" over inequalities when you add Quackers And Milk to your learning centers. Copy, color, laminate, and cut out this center. Add the directions using a permanent marker. Cut along the dotted lines. Insert a tagboard strip through the slits and program it as shown.

Convert this center to a math fact drill. Use duplicating fluid to remove the directions, and replace them using a permanent marker. Program a new strip with math problems and solutions.

Number your paper 1–10.
Write > or < .
Pull the strip down to check.

Quackers and milk

3. 18 ___ 16

Strip (left):

<
10. 94 ___ 99
>
9. 100 ___ 85
<
8. 63 ___ 68
<
7. 11 ___ 22
>
6. 20 ___ 17
>
5. 65 ___ 49
<
4. 50 ___ 80
>
3. 18 ___ 16
<
2. 69 ___ 70
>
1. 56 ___ 54

Start⬇

Start⬇

The Little Engine That Could

Get numeration skills on track with the help of this famous locomotive! Cut out ten large and ten smaller circles from construction paper. Write number words on the larger circles and numerals on the smaller ones as shown. Label ten cards with sets (or duplicate the set cards on page 171). Store all the pieces in a pocket on the back of the center. Pair up students to complete this center. Have one child place a dot set card by the whistle. Have his partner find the matching numeral and number word circles and place them on the engine. Have students switch places and continue playing.

Place a card by the whistle.
Place the matching number word and numeral circles on the engine.

The Little Engine That Could

Flying High

Clear the runway for these high-flying addition centers! Cut out several planes. Cut a slit in each and label with a number. Make several wings (to slide through the slit) and label the wings with addition problems. Students insert the wings in the correct airplanes.

Soar through other skills by making additional planes for matching upper-/lowercase letters, word pairs/contractions, or pictures/vowel sounds.

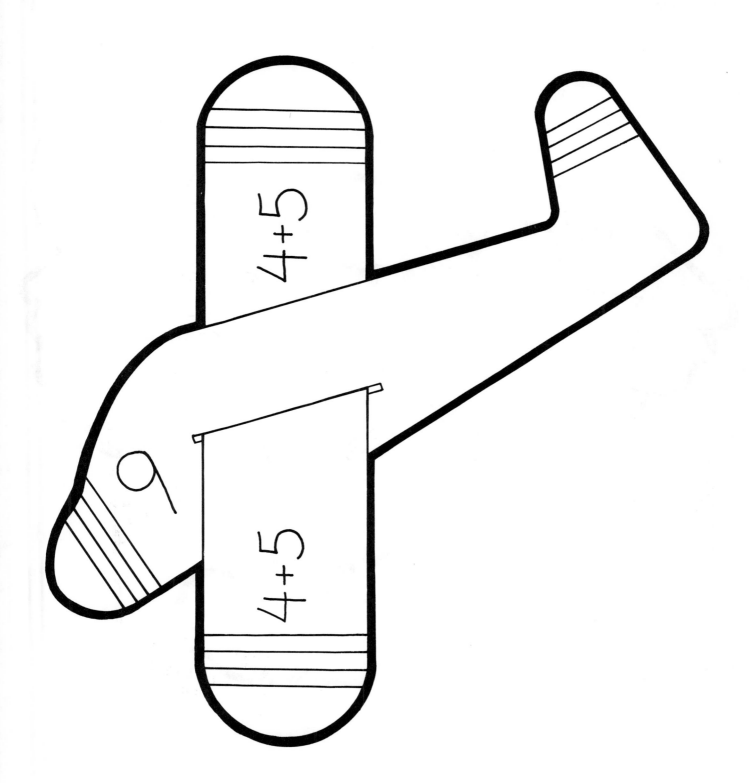

Airmail

Neither rain nor snow will keep this mailman from sorting correct and incorrect math problems! Laminate the center; then attach two pockets with rubber cement. Label cut-out cards with correct and incorrect subtraction problems. Students sort the cards into the appropriate pockets.

To change this center in a snap, peel off the pockets and rub off the excess rubber cement. Add new pockets for sorting complete/incomplete sentences, nouns/verbs, or long-/short-vowel words.

Ship Shapes

Set sail for Shape Island with this shipshape center! Label cut-out cards with shapes to match those shown on the ship. (See page 177 for a star pattern and page 169 for circle, rectangle, square, and triangle patterns.) Store the cards in a pocket attached to the back of the center.

To practice other skills, change the shapes on the sails to numbers, money amounts, blends, or parts of speech. Make cards to match.

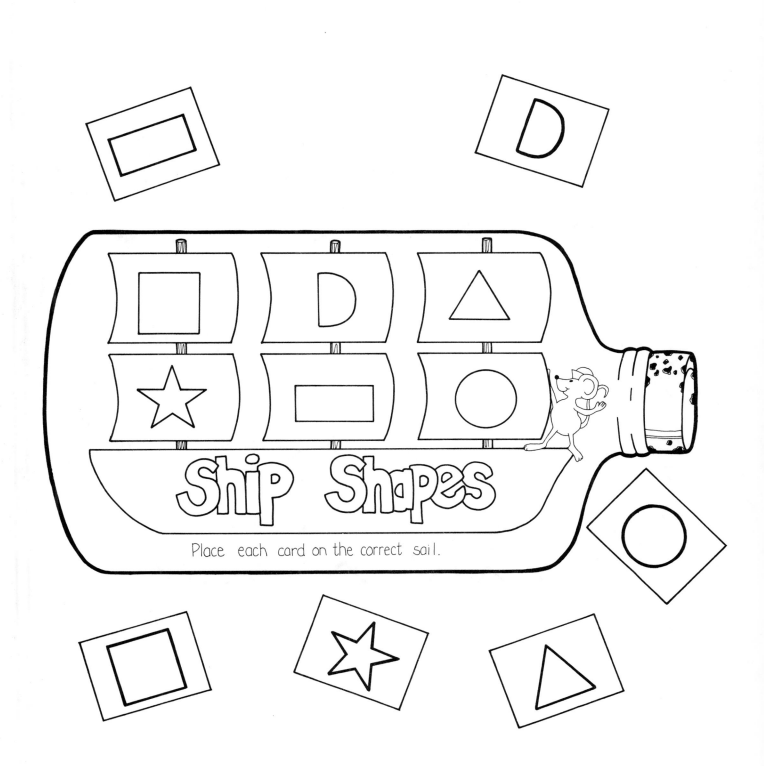

Place each card on the correct sail.

Home Tweet Home

Feather this bird's nest with addition facts! Write math facts on the nest as shown; then use a hole punch to punch out the holes. Insert a plastic drinking straw through each hole and write the answer on the back near the hole. Students poke a straw through each hole, give the answer, then flip the center to check.

For variety, program the nest with multiplication facts, singular words to spell as plurals, or words to abbreviate.

"Play It Again, Sam"

We've turned Sam's player piano into a versatile subtraction tachistoscope. Cut slits on the dotted lines where indicated. Insert a poster board strip into the slits and program it with subtraction facts and answers.

Use this center over and over again by simply changing the programmed strip. Label additional strips with spelling words with missing letters, numbers to round, or words with silent letters.

Shark!

These grinning jaws will help your students master math facts! Cut slits on the dotted lines and insert paper clips. Clip a number card to the shark's snout. Label cut-out circles with problems that equal the number on the card. Include a few "distractor" circles labeled with problems that don't equal the card's number. Store the circles in a pocket on the back of the center. Change the card and circles frequently for lots of math practice.

Dive into other skill practice by making additional cards and circles for rhyming words, categorization, parts of speech, or synonyms. Change the directions to match the skill.

Green Thumb

Plant a little flower power in your addition practice! Use the patterns on page 180 to make three flower cards. Program each card with a set of math problems. Make a slit in each pot as shown and insert the flower cards. A student pulls up a bunch of flowers to reveal addition problems to solve. To make the center self-checking, write the answers on the backs of the flower cards.

1. 27+8=   2. 6+34=
3. 7+36=   4. 92+9=

1. 12+7 =   2. 13+9=
3. 9 +16=   4. 11+19=
5. 11+2 =   6. 4 +21=

Green Thumb

Write the answer for each problem on your paper.

Then check by looking on the back of the flower card.

1. 63+9=   2. 12+2=
3. 5+46=   4. 27+3=
5. 3+34=   6. 4+25=
7. 21+7=   8. 4+77=
9. 99+1=   10. 6+81=

1. 72   2. 14
3. 51   4. 30
5. 37   6. 29
7. 28   8. 81
9. 100   10. 87

Jellybean Jar

Here's an "mm-m-m good" way to practice math skills! Color the jellybeans in the jar three or four different colors; then write appropriate tasks on cut-out cards (see examples). Attach a pocket to the front of the center to store the cards. When everyone has successfully completed the center, reward your hard workers with a real jellybean treat!

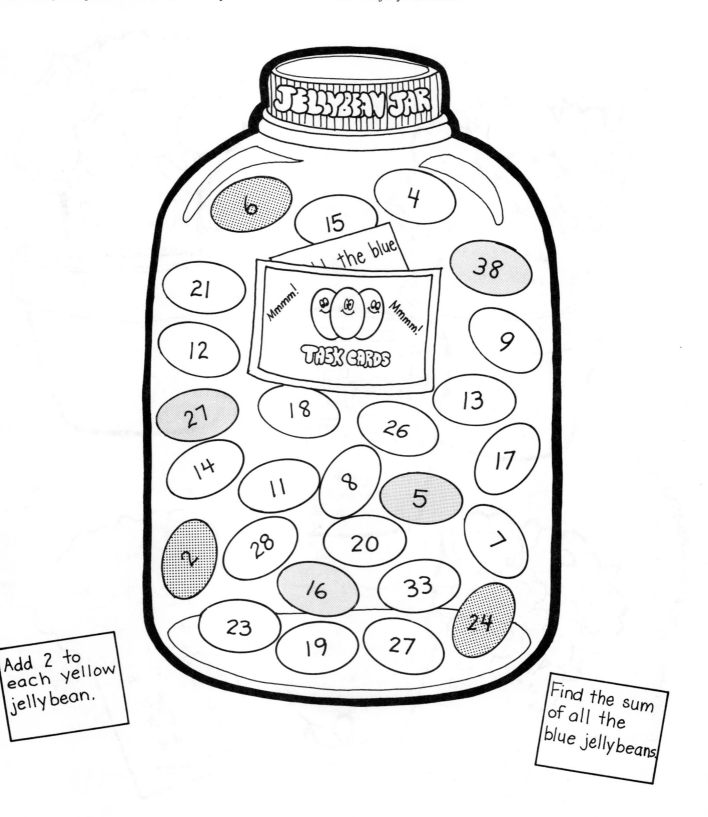

Add 2 to each yellow jellybean.

Find the sum of all the blue jellybeans.

King Midas And The Golden Touch

Color is the key to making this fun center self-checking. With a rubber stamp set (or the patterns on pages 165–167), make a set of coin cards in the amounts shown on the center. Color each money bag a different color and place a corresponding color dot on the back of each card. Store the cards in a pocket attached to the back of the center.

25¢

15¢

40¢

10¢

50¢

Help King Midas count all his money! Place each coin card on the correct money bag. Look at the color dot on the back of each card to check.

KING MIDAS and the GOLDEN TOUCH

High Seas Sailor

Sail away to improved division skills! Write answers to the problems on wooden pinch clothespins. Students clip each clothespin beside the correct problem. Store the clothespins in a Ziploc bag clipped to the center with an extra clothespin.

Adapt this center to any matching skill: upper-/lowercase letters, states/capitals, homonyms, or numbers/number words.

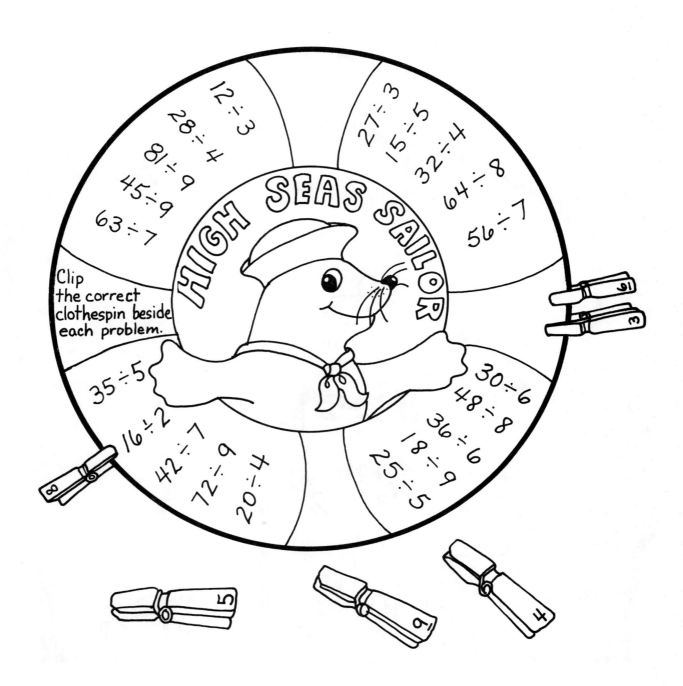

Roller Derby

Capitalize on skating's popularity with this fun numeration center. Fasten a brad beside each circle as shown. Provide seven lengths of yarn. Students match the circles by stretching each piece of yarn from one brad to another.

To make this center easy to use again, laminate it before programming the circles with a wipe-off marker. When you're ready for a change, wipe the circles clean and reprogram them with a new skill.

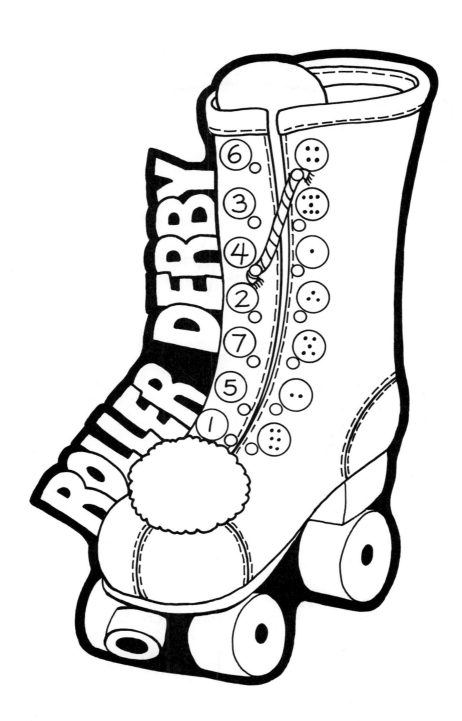

Catch A Fact

When the season for learning multiplication facts approaches, just yell, "Play ball!" Punch holes along the outside edge of this posterboard baseball glove. Write a number beside each hole and a multiplicand on the baseball. Write the correct product on the back of the center beside each hole. The student works a problem and checks his answer by poking a plastic drinking straw through the hole and turning the glove over. Change the number on the baseball frequently to give students plenty of practice.

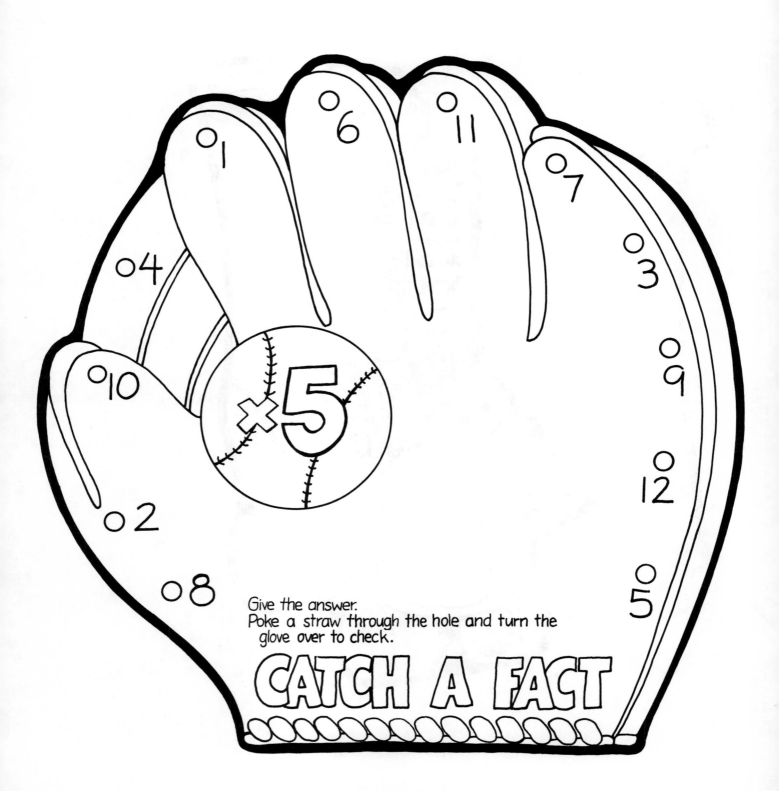

Give the answer.
Poke a straw through the hole and turn the glove over to check.

CATCH A FACT

Shower Sing-along

Here's another "poke-and-peek" center that's sure to make a splash with your students. See the instructions for how to program a poke-and-peek center and make it self-checking on page 46. Provide a plastic drinking straw for students to poke through the holes.

To get extra mileage from this center, laminate it before adding the numbers and directions with a wipe-off marker. When you're ready for a change, wipe the center clean and add new programming and directions.

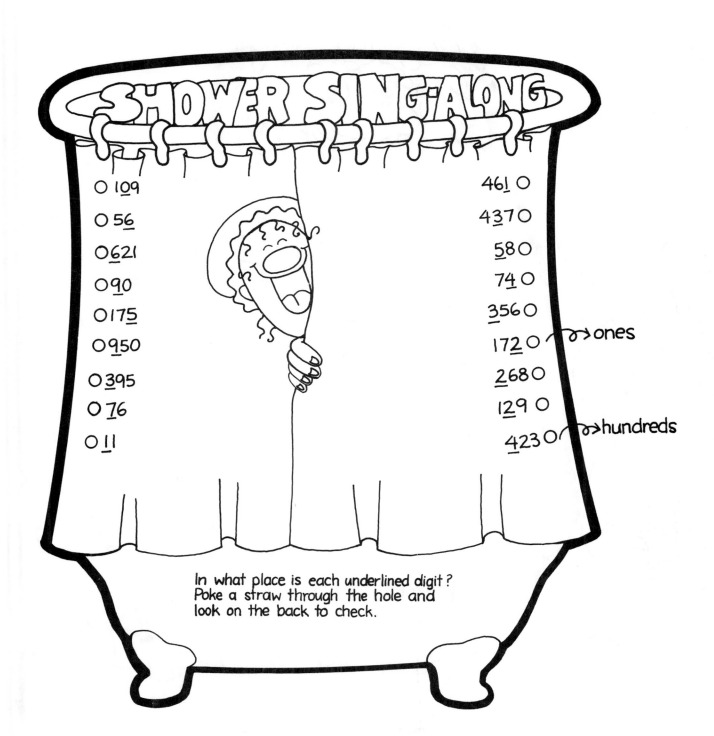

O 1<u>0</u>9

O 5<u>6</u>

O<u>6</u>21

O<u>9</u>0

O17<u>5</u>

O<u>9</u>50

O<u>3</u>95

O <u>7</u>6

O <u>1</u>1

46<u>1</u> O

43<u>7</u>O

<u>5</u>8O

7<u>4</u> O

<u>3</u>56O

17<u>2</u>O ⟶ones

<u>2</u>68O

1<u>2</u>9 O

<u>4</u>23O ⟶hundreds

In what place is each underlined digit?
Poke a straw through the hole and
look on the back to check.

Clancy

Clancy has big buttons that are bursting with addition practice! Cut out nine red circles and label them with picture sets 1–9. Cut out nine yellow circles and label them with picture sets 1–9 as well. Finally, cut out nine green circles and label them with the numerals 2–18. Store the circles, or "buttons," in a pocket attached to the back of the center. The student selects one yellow and one red button and places them on Clancy. Then he finds the matching green button to place on the clown.

Dolphin Delight

This delightful dolphin swims circles around addition problems! Use the pattern on page 179 to make the dolphin. Attach the dolphin to the Cut-out with a brad. To change problems easily, laminate the Cut-out and dolphin before programming; then write in the numbers with a wipe-off marker.

Spin the dolphin. Copy and solve each problem on your paper.

Animal Cookies

Yummy teddy bear cookies make number practice a tasty treat! Enlarge the artwork; then cut a slit in each bowl as shown. Attach one large pocket to the back of the Cut-out directly under the slits. Use the patterns on page 179 to make 30 teddy bear shapes. Write numerals 1–10 on ten bears, dot sets on ten, and number words on ten (or use the reproducible patterns on pages 171–175). Have students match the three corresponding bears and place one in each bowl.

Extend the use of this center by writing synonyms or rhyming words on the bear cutouts.

Find the three matching cookies. Put one in each bowl.

Jack 'N' The Beanstalk

Jack has his head in the clouds when it comes to math facts! Cut slits on the dotted lines and insert paper clips. Clip a number card on the giant's house. Cut out a supply of green paper leaves and label each with a math fact. Store the leaves in a pocket attached to the back of the center. Students clip on the beanstalk leaves that will match the number on the giant's house.

For variety, use this format for identifying hard-/soft-*g* words, parts of speech, or long-/short-vowel words.

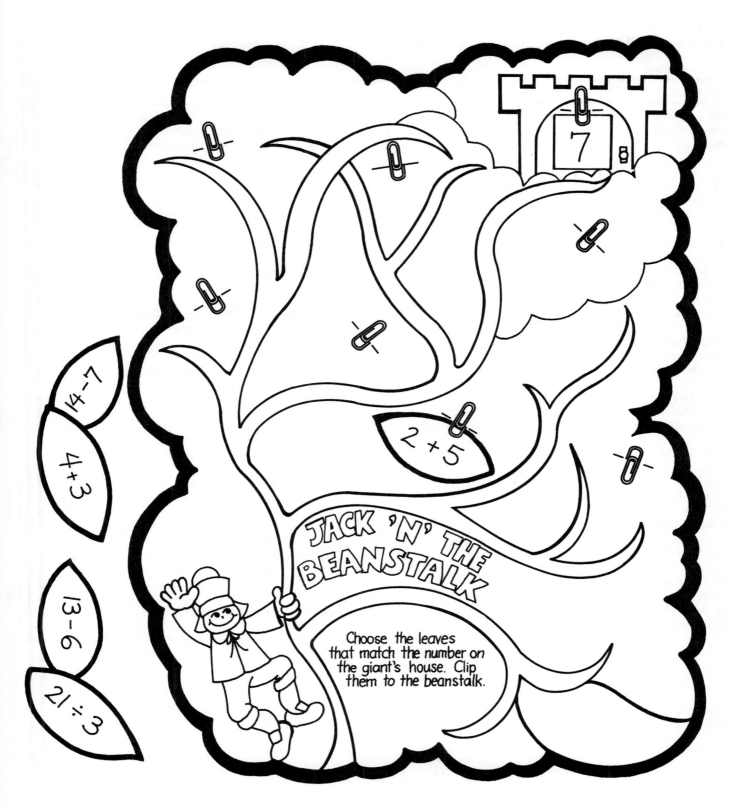

Pocket Pals

Pocket Pal learning centers are built around string-tie envelopes. (We suggest using the 9" x 12" size.) In each illustration we have shown the picture to be drawn and mounted on the front of the envelope and the instructions for the student.

All center components are stored inside the envelope, making it easy to file. Some teachers prefer storing envelopes and game card decks separately, so students can use them interchangeably. You can use a Pocket Pal for teaching a skill, for reviewing, or for involving a parent at home. Its compact size is a real bonus.

Name	Skill	Grade	Variations	Page
Hide-and-Seek	number sequence	K–1	alphabetical order, days of the week	53
Flapjack Shack	money	3–4	synonyms, division facts, abbreviations	54
Stick To It!	numbers/sets	K–1	vowels, colors/color words, math facts, contractions	55
Stir Crazy!	addition facts	1–2	contractions, abbreviations	56
Lazy Bones	greater than/less than	2–3	fact/opinion, spelling, true/false	57
Wheelin' And Dealin'	multiplication facts	2–4	addition	58
Romeo & Juliet	odd/even numbers	1–2	true/false, upper-/lowercase letters, math facts, fact/opinion	59
"There's A Monster..."	missing subtrahends	2–3	spelling, odd/even numbers, complete sentences	60
Real Stumpers	mixed math	1–3		61
Bertha's Blue Ribbons	subtraction with regrouping	2–4	addition, multiplication, division	62
Henny's Pennies	counting	K–1		63
Clowns 'n' Clocks	time to the half hour	1–2		64
Chilly Crocodillies	shapes	K–1	math facts, colors/color words, numbers/number words, states/capitals	65
Snuggle Buggles	numbers/number words/sets	K–1		66
Shuffleboard	multiplication facts	2–4	addition/subtraction facts	67
Spin The Bottle!	missing addends	2–3	rhyming words, homonyms, upper-/lowercase letters	68
Just A-Swingin'	number sequence to 25	K–1	math facts, vowels, hard-/soft-c words	69
Davy Jones's Locker	money	2–4		70
...The Teddy Train	numbers/number words/sets	K–1	math equations, colors/color words, initial or final consonants	71
"Ears" To You!	sets/number words	K–1	synonyms, homonyms, parts of speech, types of sentences	72
Snug Bugs	subtraction facts	1–2	vowels, nouns/verbs, spelling	73
Dinosaur Days	column addition	1–3	multiplication, division, synonyms, shapes	74
No Green Jelly Beans!	addition with no regrouping	2–3	subtraction, multiplication, division	75
Wow, A Purple Cow!	greater than/less than	K–1	fact/opinion, odd/even numbers, true/false, plurals/possessives	76
Float Your Boat!	addition facts	1–2	rhyming pictures, antonyms, spelling	77
Four Peas In A Pod!	place value to 1000s	3–4	parts of speech, types of sentences, food groups	78
Frankie's Fan Mail	subtraction facts	1–2	addition, blends, ending punctuation	79
Cheers!	column addition	1–3	spelling	80
The Bear Facts	multiplication facts	2–4	addition, subtraction, division, money	81
It's Showtime!	time to ten minutes	2–3		82

Hide-and-Seek

...8, 9, 10 and you're IT with this number-sequencing center! Duplicate several copies of the dragon cards on page 181 on construction paper. Label the cards with numbers to sequence; then cut them out and store them in the envelope.

Label additional dragon cards with words to alphabetize or days of the week to put in order.

HIDE-and-SEEK

Davey Dragon is IT!
Help him count to 10 by placing his friends in the correct order.

Flapjack Shack

Practice money-counting skills at this unusual pancake restaurant. After completing the artwork, label cut-out cards with coin combinations to equal the amounts shown on the envelope. Store the cards in the envelope along with an answer key.

For a change, label the flapjacks with synonyms, division facts, or abbreviations. Make matching cards.

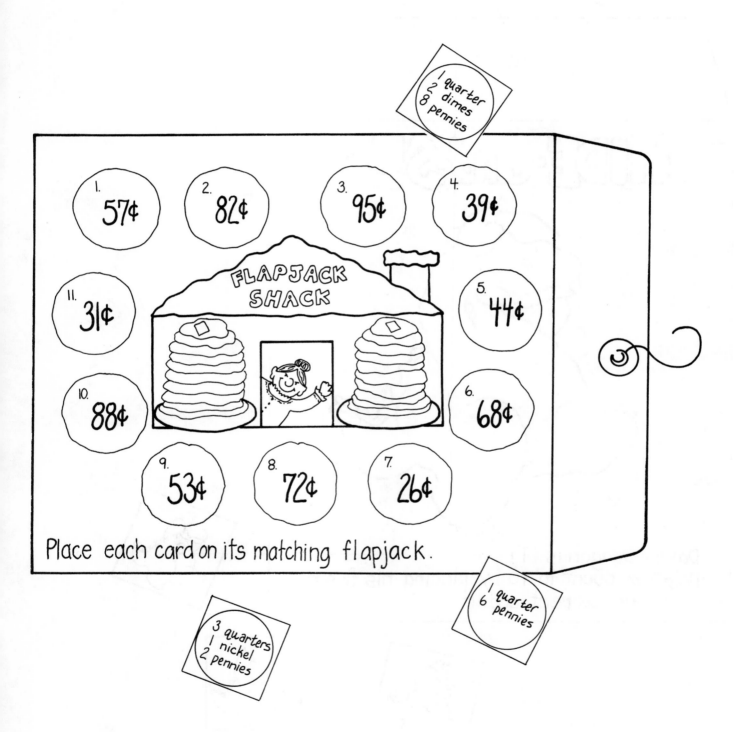

Stick To It!

Here's a clever way to recycle Popsicle sticks. With markers, label each stick with a different set. The student places each stick beside the correct numeral on the envelope. Store the sticks in the envelope.

This easy-to-make center can also be used for other matching skills: missing-vowel words/vowels, colors/color words, math facts/answers, or contractions/word pairs.

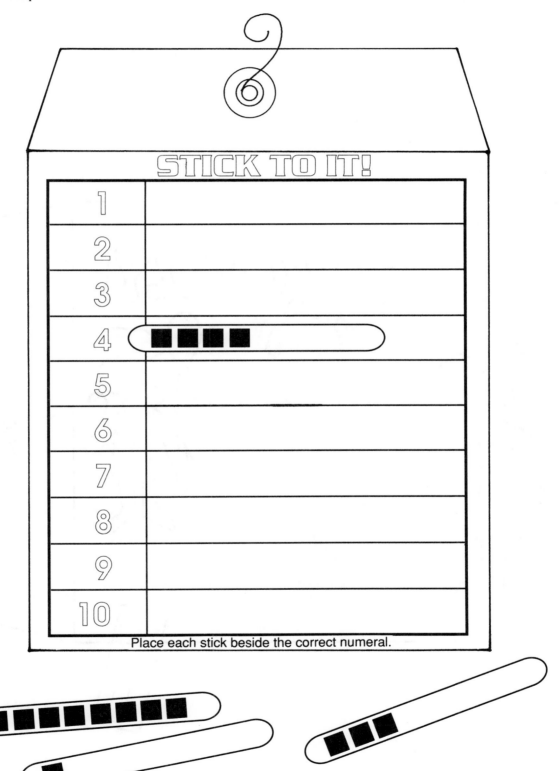

Place each stick beside the correct numeral.

Stir Crazy!

Just a spoonful of Stir Crazy makes the math fact practice go down! Duplicate several copies of the spoon cards on page 182. Mount the cards on tagboard and cut them out. Label the fronts of the cards with math facts and the backs with corresponding answers. Store the spoon cards in the envelope.

Stir in more skill practice by labeling additional spoon cards with word pairs to write as contractions or words to abbreviate. Change the directions.

Solve each problem on your paper. Turn the spoons over to check.

©1991 The Education Center, Inc.

Lazy Bones

These snoozing canines may nap right through all the numeration practice this center provides! Duplicate several copies of the bone cards on page 182. Mount the cards on tagboard and cut them out. Label the cards with < and > number sentences as shown. Store the bone cards in the envelope.

To get more use from this center, reprogram the doghouses and make new bone cards labeled with fact/opinion statements, incorrect/correct spelling words, or true/false statements.

Wheelin' And Dealin'

Students will enjoy practicing multiplication facts from this center. Copy the artwork and mount it on an envelope. Write the directions on the back of the envelope and laminate. Attach a spinner to each wheel. Laminate a multiplication table and store it in the envelope with 40 game chips.

With the same gameboard, have younger students add. Provide an addition answer key.

Directions for 2-4 players:

1. In turn, spin each spinner.
2. Write down the numbers spun and multiply.
3. Check your answer with the key.
4. If correct, earn one chip.
5. The first person to earn ten chips wins!

Romeo & Juliet

Practice identifying odd and even numbers with the help of this loving couple. Use the heart patterns on page 178 to make a set of cutouts labeled with odd and even numbers. To make the activity self-checking, code the backs of the odd-numbered hearts with a "J" for Juliet and the backs of the even-numbered ones with an "R" for Romeo. Store the hearts in the envelope.

Romeo and Juliet are also a great pair to help students sort true/false statements, upper-/lowercase letters, correct/incorrect math facts, or facts/opinions.

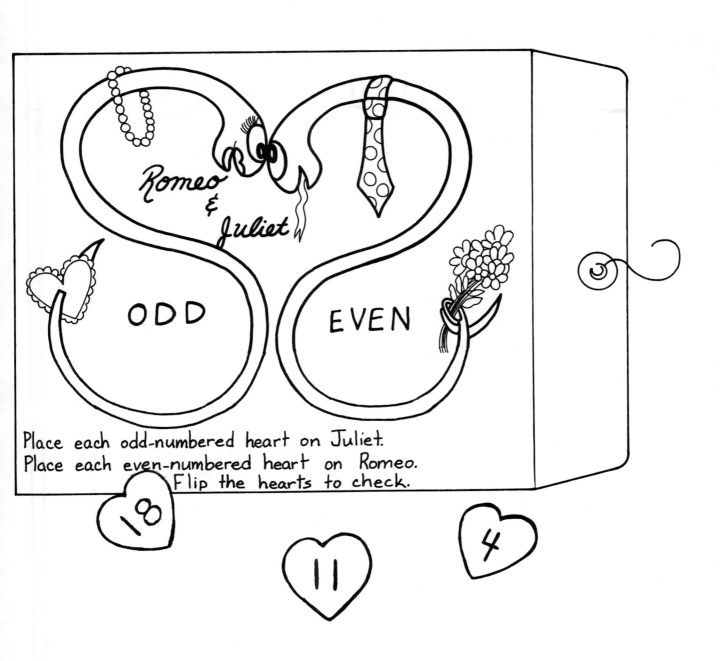

"There's A Monster Under My Mattress!"

Monstrous fun is in store for your students as they improve their subtraction skills. To make this learning center, copy the artwork and directions, mount them on an envelope, and laminate. Use the pattern given to make 30 tagboard cards. Laminate the tagboard cards and program them with missing-subtrahend problems, using a wipe-off marker. Store the cards in the envelope along with an answer key.

This versatile center can be easily adapted to reinforce a variety of skills. Change the directions and reprogram the cards for practice with: correct/incorrect spellings, even/odd numbers, complete/incomplete sentences. Code the backs of the cards with answers for self-checking.

Pattern

Directions for 2 players:
1. Choose a bed.
2. Place cards in a stack problem side up.
3. In turn, draw a card.
    If you fill in the blank correctly, place the card under your mattress. If incorrect, discard the card.
4. The player with the most cards under his mattress at the end of the game wins!

Real Stumpers

Don't let these mixed-math butterflies get away! Color four butterflies each of these colors: red, yellow, blue, and green. Then store cut-out task cards in the envelope (see examples below). Students take a card and follow its directions.

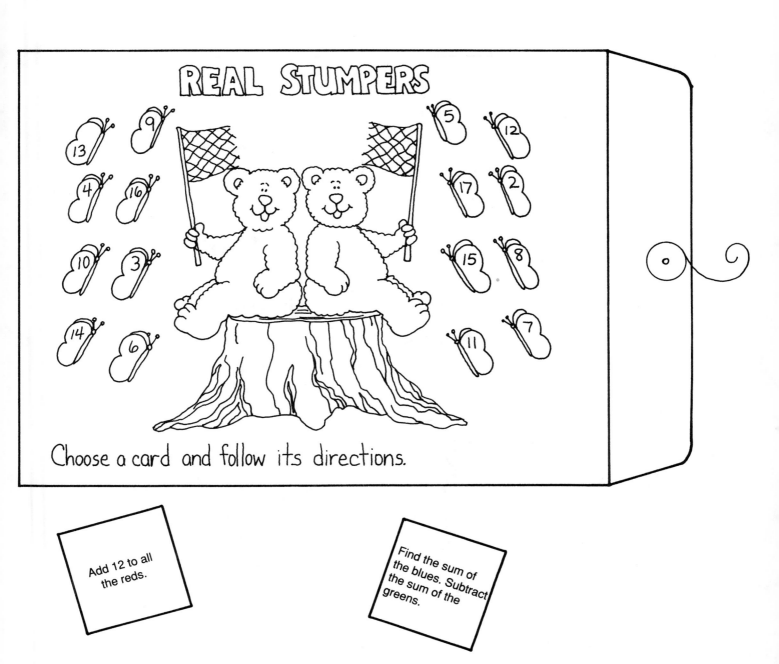

REAL STUMPERS

Choose a card and follow its directions.

Add 12 to all the reds.

Find the sum of the blues. Subtract the sum of the greens.

Bertha's Blue Ribbons

Bertha's trophy will be covered with ribbons at the end of this activity. Label ribbon cards (see page 182) with correct and incorrect subtraction problems. Code the backs of the cards *I* or *C* for self-checking.

To switch to other skills, prepare new sets of ribbon cards and new directions if needed.

Place the ribbons with correct answers on the trophy.

Turn the ribbons over to check.

Bertha's Blue Ribbons

$$\begin{array}{r} 32 \\ -29 \\ \hline 3 \end{array}$$

$$\begin{array}{r} 24 \\ -19 \\ \hline 5 \end{array}$$

1st

Henny's Pennies

Help Henny count her bright, shiny pennies with this appealing activity. After completing the artwork, attach a spinner to the envelope. Use the patterns on page 165 to make at least ten penny cards, or use real pennies. Students spin and count out the correct number of pennies. Store the pennies in the envelope.

Clowns 'n' Clocks

Give these clowns a hand for time-telling practice. Copy the artwork, attach it to the envelope, and laminate. Cut out 12 tagboard cards as shown. Program each card with a digital time to correspond to one of the clocks on the center. Store the pieces in the envelope. Vary the use of this center by providing cards with times expressed in words.

Chilly Crocodillies

These cold creatures are keeping warm with shape-decorated earmuffs. Cut out 14–20 paper circles. Draw identical shapes on pairs of circles. Attach a pipe cleaner to one circle from each pair. Store the pieces in the envelope.

Make more earmuffs for other matching skills such as math facts/answers, colors/color words, numbers/number words, or states/capitals.

Snuggle Buggles

Snuggle these bugs into beds for practice with numbers, number words, and sets. Copy the artwork, attach it to an envelope, and laminate. Make ten copies of the cards on page 181. Program the cards with numbers, number words, and sets as shown. Mount the cards on tagboard, laminate, and cut out. Program the backs for self-checking using a permanent marker. Store the cards in the envelope.

Find the matching bed, bug, and blanket for each number.

66

Shuffleboard

Your students will love the exciting fun of Shuffleboard! Label 30 tagboard cards with multiplication problems. Provide a game chip, wooden nickel, or coin suitable for "thumping" across the envelope's shuffleboard. (Or try folding a piece of paper into a thick triangle and taping the ends together.) Store the cards, an answer key or multiplication table, a copy of the student directions, and the "thumper" in the envelope.

Directions for 2 players:
1. Draw a card and give the answer.
2. Check the key. If correct, place the marker behind the starting line and "thump" it onto the shuffleboard to score points. If the marker goes off the board, you do not score. If it lands on a line between two points, thump again.
3. At the end of the game, add up your points. The player with the highest total wins!

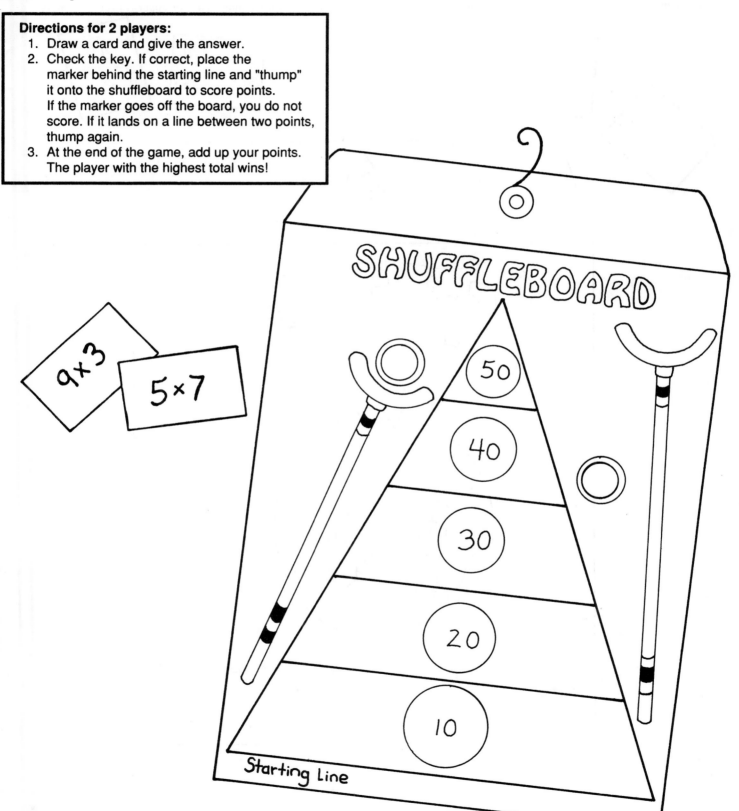

Spin The Bottle!

This center for missing-addend problems is not for the dizzy-headed! Copy the artwork, attach it to an envelope, and laminate. Duplicate several copies of the cards on page 183. Mount them on tagboard and cut them out. Number the genie cards and program them with missing-addend problems. Label the bottle cards with the missing addends. Provide an answer key and store it in the envelope with the cards.

Change the programming for this magical center to use it for matching rhyming words, homonyms, or upper-/lowercase letters.

©1991 The Education Center, Inc.

Just A-Swingin'

Sharpen sequencing concepts with these swingin' apes! Label cut-out cards with correct and incorrect number sequences as shown. For self-checking, code the backs of the cards with **I** and **C**. Have students place each card on the correct swing.

Use this activity for a variety of sorting skills: correct/incorrect math facts, long-/short-vowel words, numbers greater than/less than 10, or hard-/soft-*c* words.

Davy Jones's Locker

Determine the value of the coins in Davy's locker for money skills practice. Copy the artwork, attach it to the envelope, and laminate. Make several copies of the coin cards on page 184. Number the cards; then program them with money amounts as shown. Mount the cards on tagboard, laminate, and cut out. Store the cards with an answer key in the envelope.

To vary the use of this center, provide cards with coin stamps to be counted.

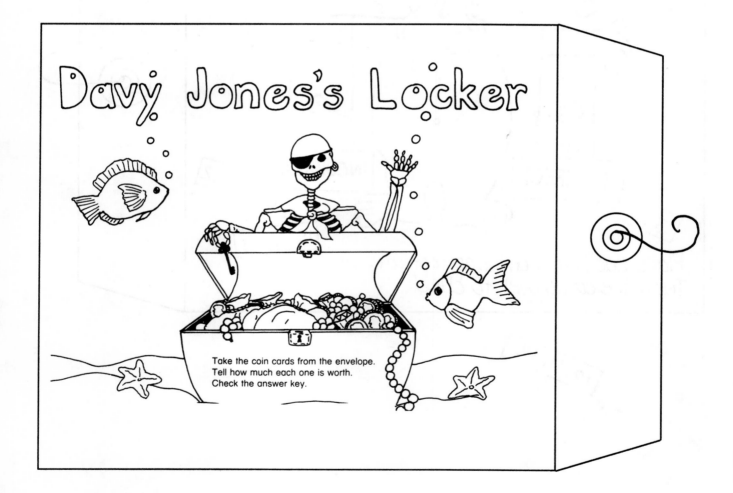

All Aboard The Teddy Train

All aboard for a trainload of number matching! Copy the artwork and the directions, mount them on an envelope, and laminate. Make tagboard cards "bearing" numerals, dot sets, and number words (see the patterns on pages 171–175). Laminate the cards before storing them in the envelope.

Consider making additional cards to entice students to practice matching math problems with solutions, colors with color words, and initial or final consonants with pictures.

Place the matching cards on the train cars.

All Aboard The Teddy Train

"Ears" To You!

"Ears" a numeration activity that will keep students hopping. Copy the artwork and mount it on the front of an envelope; copy the directions and mount them on the back. Using the patterns provided, make 20 tagboard cards (10 gifts and 10 gift tags). Laminate the envelope and cards. Using a permanent marker, program the gift and gift tag cards with matching sets and number words. Code the backs of the cards for self-checking. Store all the cards in the envelope.

Change the programming on the center and the cards for other matching activities, including synonyms, antonyms, homonyms, parts of speech, or types of sentences.

Directions:
Take the gifts and gift tags out of the envelope.
Look at the sets on the gifts.
Match them to the number words on the tags.
Turn them over to check.

Patterns

Snug Bugs

Correct subtraction facts keep these shivering insects warm! Cut slits in the rug as shown and insert paper clips. Label cut-out cards with correct and incorrect subtraction facts. Code the backs of the cards for self-checking. Store the fact cards in the envelope.

Snug Bugs will also warm up other skills such as long/short vowels, nouns/verbs, and incorrect/correct spelling words.

Help these icy insects get warm! Clip on only correct rugs.
Look on the backs of the rugs to check.

Dinosaur Days

Students will enjoy matching dinosaur egg halves containing math problems and answers. Copy the artwork, attach it to an envelope, and laminate. Make several copies of the eggshell cards on page 184. Program the cards with column addition problems and answers. Mount the cards on tagboard, laminate, and cut out. Store the cards and an answer key in the envelope.

Change the answer key and make new eggshell cards for addition, multiplication, or division practice. Or program the cards with synonyms, colors/color words, or shapes to match.

Match the eggshells to hatch a batch of dinosaur eggs.
Check the key.

No Green Jelly Beans!

While working with this activity, youngsters will get the feeling they're just monkeying around—but you'll have the satisfaction of knowing they're improving their addition skills. Copy the artwork and directions, mount them on an envelope, and laminate. Then use the pattern to make jelly bean addition cards on green tagboard as shown. Provide an answer key. Laminate the cards and the key before storing them in the envelope.

Your students will never outgrow this center if you update it periodically with addition, subtraction, multiplication, or division skill cards to match their math mastery levels.

Pattern

2. $11 + 18$

1. $30 + 6$

17. $23 + 14$

No Green Jelly Beans!

Help fill the bag with green jelly beans.
1. Take a card.
2. Work the problem on your paper.
3. Check with the answer key.
4. If correct, put the card on the bag.
Ten green jelly beans will fill the bag!

18. $25 + 22$

16. $41 + 24$

10. $56 + 40$

8. $15 + 32$

Wow, A Purple Cow!

Once you've seen a purple cow, you've seen everything! Label tagboard cards with missing-symbol math sentences as shown. For self-checking, write > or < on the back of each card. Store the cards in the envelope.

Let this colorful cow help your students sort other cards labeled with facts/opinions, odd/even numbers, true/false statements, or plurals/possessives.

31 ____ 13

11 ____ 13

<

>

<

Place each card on the right milk can.
Turn the cards over to check.

Float Your Boat!

Even landlubbers will love the math facts practice on board this center! Duplicate several copies of the boat and sail patterns on page 183. Mount the patterns on tagboard; then cut them out. Label the sails with math problems and the boats with answers to match. Code the backs of the pieces for self-checking.

Set sail for more skills practice by making additional boats and sails programmed with rhyming pictures, antonyms, or spelling words/definitions.

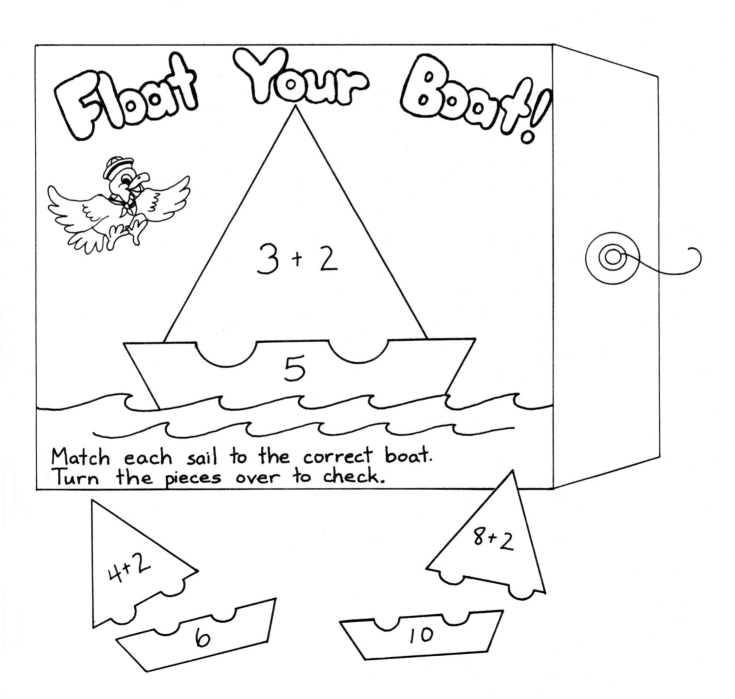

Four Peas In A Pod!

These cheerful peas in a pod encourage your students to do some place-value practice. Copy the artwork and attach it to an envelope. Write the directions on the back of the envelope before laminating it. Provide 20 green cards as shown. Write a number in which one digit has been underlined on each card. Laminate and cut out the cards. Using a permanent marker, program the backs for self-checking.

Change the programming, directions, and cards to use this activity for practice with parts of speech, types of sentences, or the four food groups.

Directions:

1. Look at the underlined digit on each card.
2. Place each card on the correct pea.
3. Flip the cards to check.

Frankie's Fan Mail

Real envelopes will make this subtraction center a real treat. Write subtraction problems on the fronts of small envelopes. To make the activity self-checking, write the answer to each problem on the inside flap of the envelope. Store the small envelopes in the Pocket Pal.

This versatile format can be used with a wide variety of skills: addition, multiplication, ending punctuation, homonyms, blends, and initial consonants.

Cheers!

Bottoms up for addition drill! Draw these mugs of root beer on the front of an envelope and cut a slit across the top of each. Label poster board strips with correct and incorrect column addition problems, coding the backs of the strips with *I* or *C* for self-checking. Store the strips inside the envelope.

Make new strips for other correct and incorrect math facts or spelling words when your students need a change.

The Bear Facts

Here's a "beary" good enticement to motivate your students to practice multiplication facts. Copy the artwork and directions, and mount them on an envelope. Laminate the envelope and attach a spinner to the circle. Using the bear card patterns on page 184, make 35 tagboard cards and program them with multiplication problems. Write the answers on the backs of the cards for self-checking before laminating. Store the cards in the envelope.

The Bear Facts works equally well for addition, subtraction, and division practice. Or convert this center for money-counting practice by using coin stamps on the bear cards. Students count and determine the values of the coin combinations and play as before.

This game is for 2 players. Place cards problem side up.

At the same time, each player draws a card and says the answer.
One player spins to see if the high or low answer wins.
The winner gets both cards.
The player with the most cards at the end wins!

It's Showtime!

Sprinkle a little magic into your math instruction with this appealing activity on telling time. Duplicate the blank clock face cards on page 163 on construction paper. Cut out the cards; then add clock hands on each (being sure that the earliest time is 8:00 a.m.). Write the matching digital time on the back of each clock card for self-checking. Store the cards in the envelope.

9:30

IT'S SHOWTIME!

When will the Great Hare-dini perform? Put the clocks in order beginning with 8:00 a.m. Then write the times in order on your paper. Turn the clocks over to check.

The Great Hare-dini!
First Show at 8:00 a.m.
Last Show at 8:00 p.m.

6:20

Clip-ons

Clip-ons are made from 17" x 22" sheets of poster board. After the artwork is complete and laminated, you slit on the dotted lines and add paper clips. (Colored clips add a special touch.) Accompanying cards or pieces are programmed to match the skill shown and stored in a pocket on the back of the center.

Use Clip-ons on a bulletin board, the door, or a table. Since these figures have universal appeal and aren't seasonal, make them reusable by programming the figures with a permanent marker after lamination or by providing several sets of matching cards.

Name	Skill	Grade	Variations	Page
Rainbow Gold	sets/number words	K–1	rhyming words, antonyms, math facts, initial consonants	84
Rock 'n' Roll With Ronnie Rat	rounding numbers	2–4	rhyming words, synonyms, antonyms, homonyms, states/capitals	85
Lovely Ladybug	sets/numbers	K–1		86
Quack's Snack Attack	subtraction	1–2	fact/opinion, rhyming words, antonyms	87
Clown Time	time to five minutes	3–4		88
Cricket Thicket	addition with regrouping	2–3	spelling, punctuation, capitalization, division	89
Desert Rats	odd/even numbers	1–2	antonyms, synonyms	90
Pop-up Piggy	money	1–2	numbers/number words, ordinal/cardinal number words, cause/effect	91
Don't Be Late!	number sequence	K–1		92
Cold Cash!	money	1–2		93
What A Wingding!	subtraction facts	1–2	complete sentences, odd/even numbers	94
Shower Power	multiplication facts	2–4	addition, subtraction, punctuation, spelling, capitalization	95
The Lion & The Mouse	mixed math	2–3	rhyming pictures, blends, states/capitals, homonyms	96
Sweet Sixteen	two-step equations	2–3	complete sentences, spelling, vowels	97
USS Seed	place value to 1000s	2–3	upper-/lowercase letters, rhyming words, contractions	98
Leopard Luck	missing addends	2–3	subtraction, multiplication	99
Plumber's Helper	number sequence	K–1	alphabet sequence, alphabetical order, story sequence	100
…Hooverville Hummingbirds	greater than/less than	1–2	math sentences	101
Math Motel	addition/subtraction facts	1–2	multiplication	102
Silver Dollar Pancakes	money	2–3		103

Rainbow Gold

Somewhere over the rainbow, there's numeration practice that's worth its weight in gold! Cut slits along the dotted lines and insert paper clips. Use a bright yellow or metallic gold marker to draw sets from 1–10 on ten cut-out cards. Clip the cards to the center.

Use this format for other one-to-one matching skills: rhyming words, antonyms, math facts/answers, pictures/initial consonants.

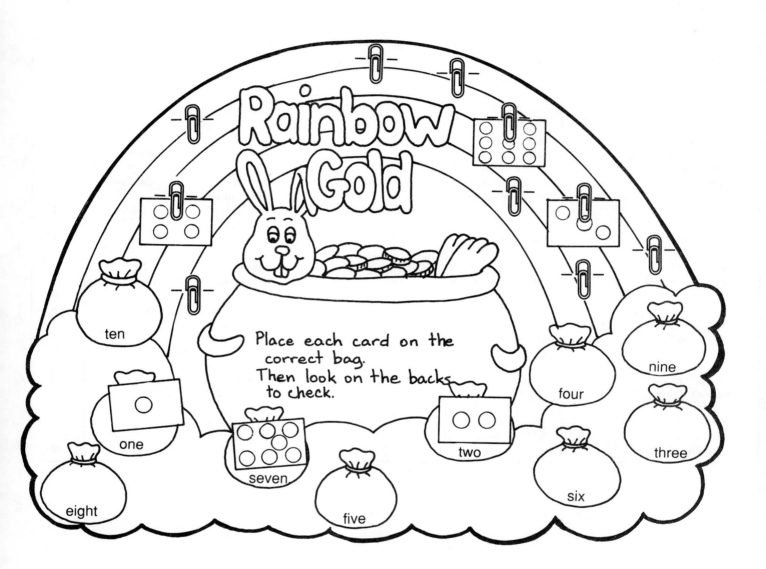

ten

one

eight

seven

five

two

four

six

nine

three

Place each card on the correct bag.
Then look on the backs to check.

Rock 'n' Roll With Ronnie Rat

Students rock 'n' roll while they round numbers to the nearest ten and 100. Copy the artwork, programming, and directions. Laminate. Slit on the dotted lines and insert paper clips. Provide 18 tagboard cards, as shown, labeled with rounded numbers to match the center. Also provide an answer key. Laminate the cards and key before storing them in a pocket on the back of the center.

Change the programming, directions, and cards to have students match rhyming words, synonyms, antonyms, homonyms, or states and capitals.

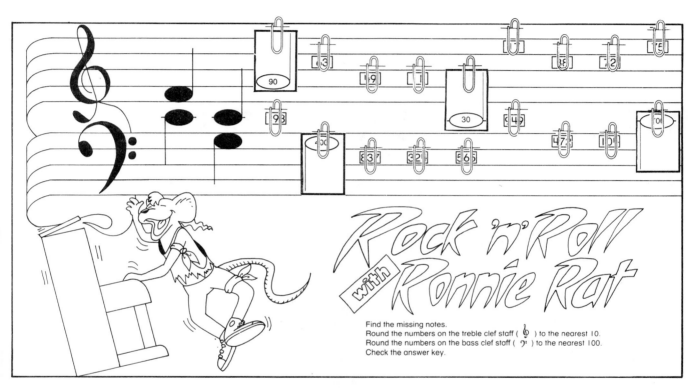

Find the missing notes.
Round the numbers on the treble clef staff (𝄞) to the nearest 10.
Round the numbers on the bass clef staff (𝄢) to the nearest 100.
Check the answer key.

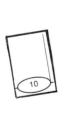
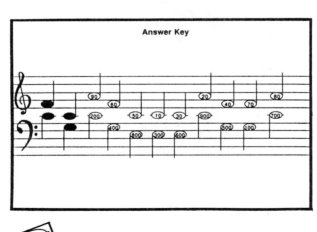

Lovely Ladybug

Turn this lovely ladybug into a numeration game for two. Cut slits where indicated and insert paper clips. Cut out 20 circles the same size as the circles on the ladybug. Label ten of the circles with sets from 1–10 and ten with matching numerals. Store the circles in a pocket on the back of the center.

To play, each player takes one side of the ladybug. The circles are placed facedown in a pile. In turn, players draw a circle. The numerals on the ladybug are covered by sets and the sets are covered by numerals. The first player to cover all the spots on his side of the ladybug wins.

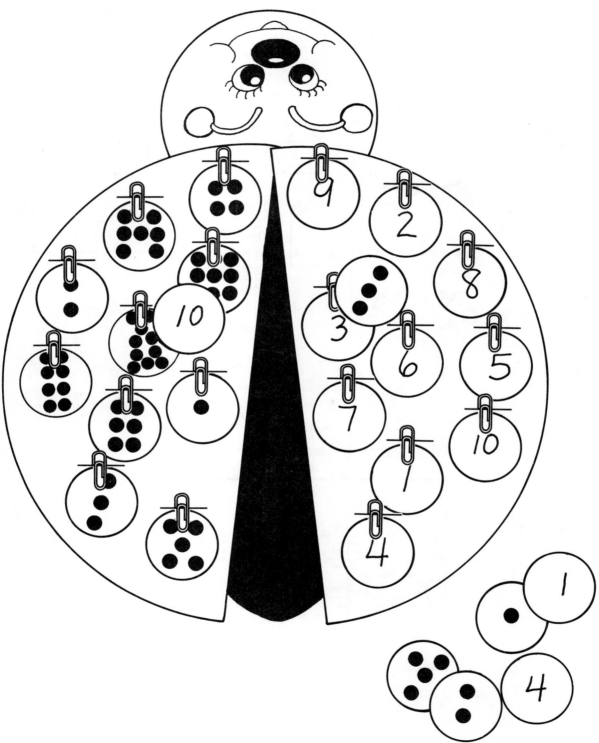

Quack's Snack Attack

Students should feed Quack only the cookies that show correct math equations. Copy the artwork and directions. Laminate. Slit on the dotted lines and insert paper clips. Provide 12 tagboard cards (patterns on page 185) with correct equations on them and eight with ones that are incorrect. Program the backs of the cards with *C* or *I* for self-checking before laminating. Store the cards in a pocket on the back of the center.

Other variations using this correct/incorrect format: facts and opinions, rhyming words, antonyms, or synonyms.

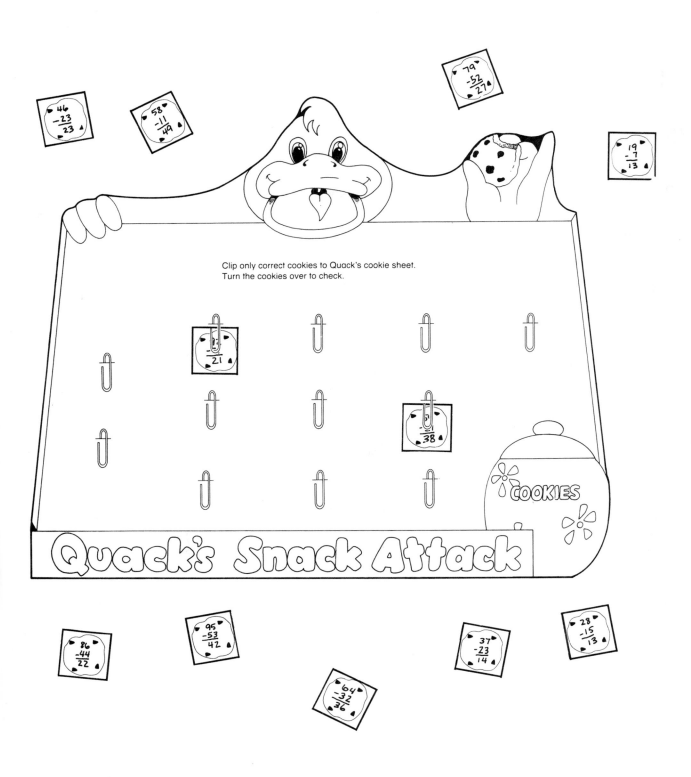

Clip only correct cookies to Quack's cookie sheet.
Turn the cookies over to check.

Clown Time

The timing is just perfect for telling time in five-minute intervals. Copy the artwork and directions. Using a clock-face stamp and a felt-tip marker, add clock faces as shown. Laminate. Slit on the dotted lines and insert paper clips. Prepare tagboard cards (see the clown card patterns on page 185) with digital times to match the center. Laminate the cards, and store them in a pocket on the back of the center.

Vary the skill level of this center by numbering the clocks and having students write the times on their own papers.

Cricket Thicket

Deep in this insect jungle, you'll find plenty of addition practice! Cut slits on the dotted lines and insert paper clips. Label cut-out cards with correct and incorrect addition equations. Code the backs of the cards with *C* or *I* for self-checking. Store the cards in a pocket on the back of the center.

By changing the cards, you can use Cricket Thicket to brush up on a variety of skills. Try spelling, punctuation, multiplication, subtraction, division, or capitalization.

Clip only correct cards to the blades of grass.
Turn the cards over to check.

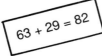

63 + 29 = 82

83 + 19 = 102

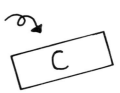

C

Desert Rats

Students get into some prickly odd/even practice with this cactus center. After completing the artwork, laminate and cut out the center. Slit on the dotted lines. Slide a paper clip into each slit. Label a set of cards one through 20. Code the backs for self-checking, laminate, and cut out. Store the cards in a pocket on the back of the center.

For language arts practice, change the directions to read, "Clip only antonyms to the catcus." Provide cards with pairs of antonyms and synonyms, and program the backs for self-checking.

Clip only <u>odd</u> numbers to the cactus.
Turn cards over to check.

Pop-up Piggy

Students match sets of coins to values for money-counting practice in Piggy's center. Copy the artwork, programming, and directions. Laminate. Slit on the dotted lines and insert paper clips. Use coin stamps or the patterns on pages 165–167 to make tagboard cards showing matching sets of coins. Laminate the cards before programming the backs for self-checking using a permanent marker. Store the cards in a pocket on the back of the center.

Change the directions, programming, and cards to have students match numbers to number words, ordinal number words to cardinal number words, or causes with effects.

Don't Be Late!

Your youngsters will rush to this number-sequencing center, with its bright red schoolhouse. Cut slits where indicated and insert paper clips. Cut out 15 small cards the same size as the spaces on the game trail; then label them with the numbers that are missing from the trail. Store the cards in a pocket on the back of the center.

Clip the number cards on the trail correctly.

Cold Cash!

Students match money values to sets of coins in the "Cold Cash" center. Copy the artwork and directions. Use rubber money stamps or the reproducible patterns on pages 165–167 for the coins. Laminate. Slit on the dotted lines and insert paper clips. Use the patterns on page 185 to provide 18 tagboard cards labeled with money values that match the sets of coins. Provide an answer key. Laminate the cards and key before storing them in a pocket on the back of the center.

Convert this center so that students match sets of coins to money values.

What A Wingding!

Subtraction practice seems like a celebration with this wingding of a center. Complete the artwork and laminate. Slit along the dotted lines and insert paper clips. Label the cards with correct and incorrect math facts. Code the backs of the cards for self-checking and laminate. Store the cards in a pocket attached to the back of the center.

Substitute other sets of cards and modify the directions to have students discriminate between complete/incomplete sentences, odd/even numbers, or sets of antonyms/synonyms.

9-2=7

What A Wingding !

Clip correct problems on the balloons.
Turn the cards over to check.

8-4=5 or I

Shower Power

Here's a great way to reinforce multiplication facts. Cut slits along the dotted lines and insert paper clips. Label cut-out circles with incorrect and correct multiplication facts. Store the circles in a pocket on the back of the center.

To provide practice in other skills, simply provide a new set of cards for addition, subtraction, punctuation, spelling, or capitalization. Modify the directions if necessary.

Kazimoto loves his polka-dotted shower curtain! Clip only dots labeled with correct problems and answers to the curtain.

The Lion & The Mouse

Bite by bite, your students will eagerly solve math problems to free this desperate lion from the net. Cut slits along the dotted lines and insert paper clips. Cut or tear construction paper into 25 "nibble markers" as shown. Label each marker with an answer to one of the problems on the net. Store the markers and an answer key in a pocket attached to the back of the center.

Aesop's "odd couple" can make other math skills fun to practice. Label the center and markers to match rhyming pictures, blends/missing-blend words, states/capitals, words/abbreviations, Roman numerals/Arabic numerals, or homonyms.

Sweet Sixteen

Chef Tail has a sweet tooth for correct math equations! Copy the artwork. Cut slits along the dotted lines and insert paper clips. Label 16 cut-out cards with correctly solved, two-step equations (see examples). Label eight to ten additional cards with incorrect equations. Mount all the cards on tagboard; then laminate and cut them out. Store the cards in a pocket on the back of the center.

Extend the usefulness of this center by programming additional card sets with correct/incorrect spelling words, complete/incomplete sentences, or long-/short-vowel cards.

USS Seed

Your students will find smooth sailing as they practice recognizing place value! Copy the artwork, programming, and directions. Laminate. Slit on the dotted lines and insert paper clips. Label 15 tagboard cards (patterns on page 186) with the numbers shown in the answer key. Provide an answer key. Laminate the cards and key. Attach a pocket to the back of the center to store the cards and key.

To vary the center, change the cards and the programming on the center so that the place values appear on the cards, and the numbers are on the center. Or use for matching upper-/lowercase letters, rhyming words, or contractions/word pairs.

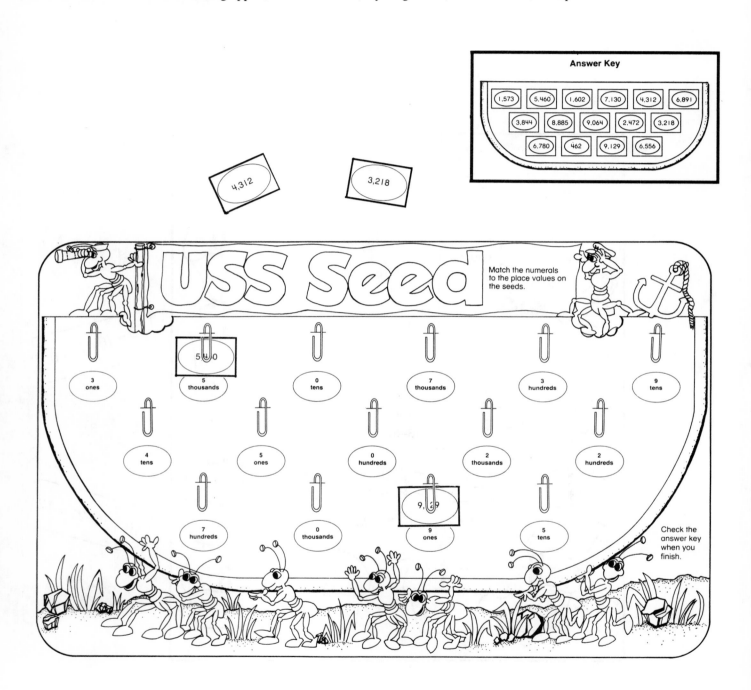

Leopard Luck

Help this unlucky leopard regain his spots. Cut slits on the dotted lines and insert paper clips. Draw a series of small circles on white paper. Label each circle with an addend for one of the problems on the leopard. Glue the white paper to a sheet of black construction paper; then laminate the sheet and cut out the circles. Store the circles in a pocket on the back of the center. Students clip each answer to the correct problem, then turn over the circles to give the leopard his spots.

Plumber's Helper

Most students need plenty of work in sequencing, and Plumber's Helper fills the bill. Cut slits along the dotted lines and insert paper clips. Prepare a set of cards labeled with numbers or ordinal words to sequence. Store the cards in a pocket on the back of the center.

Put Plumber's Helper to work sequencing letters of the alphabet, words, story events, or number words too.

Presenting The Hooverville Hummingbirds

Hooverville Hummingbirds is a humdinger of an inequalities center. Copy the artwork, directions, and programming. Laminate. Slit on the dotted lines and insert paper clips. Prepare tagboard cards with inequality symbols. Laminate the cards, and store them in a pocket on the back of the center along with a laminated answer key.

Convert this center so that students match operation symbols to math sentences without operation symbols.

Math Motel

Great for small group review, Math Motel involves three students. Two "guests" choose fact cards and "check them into" (clip them on) the correct rooms; one "innkeeper" makes a room check to insure that each card is clipped to the correct door. Cut slits along the dotted lines and insert paper clips. Label one set of cards with addition problems and another with subtraction problems with answers to match the room numbers. Store the cards in pockets attached to the front of the center.

Directions for 2–3 students:
If you are a "guest," clip each card to the correct room.
If you are the "innkeeper," check to be sure that each card is clipped to the correct room.

Silver Dollar Pancakes

This center will have your students flipping for money-counting practice. Copy the artwork; then color, laminate, and cut it out. Use a rubber stamp set or the reproducible patterns on pages 165–167 to make a set of coin cards (see examples). Mount the cards on tagboard, laminate, and cut out. Code the backs of the cards for self-checking with a permanent marker. Attach a bandana to the front of the center. Fold it to form a pocket, and place the coin cards inside.

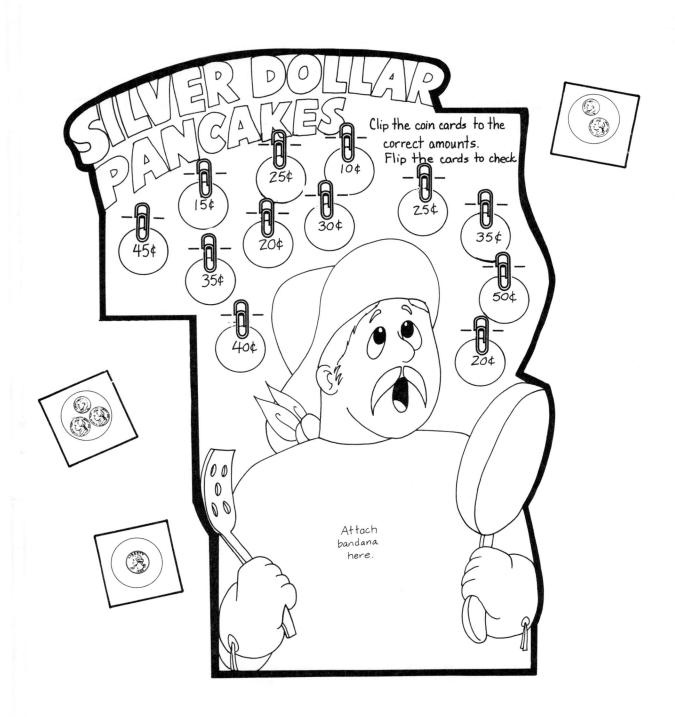

File Folders

Storage is the big advantage to the file folder format. We suggest using white folders with a straight cut, but any color and cut will work. Be on the lookout for magazine pictures, stickers, or any type of illustration that would simplify the construction process. If you laminate the file folder, a student can work directly on it with a wipe-off crayon; or you can ask students to write answers on a separate sheet of paper. Because the file folder is small enough to be used at the student's desk, you can have many activities going on at the same time.

Name	Skill	Grade	Variations	Page
Monster Mouth	subtraction facts	1–2	fact/opinion, upper-/lowercase letters, hard-/soft-c, synonyms, antonyms	105
Drumstick Drill	counting	K–1		106
Fancy Pants	shapes	K–1		107
Lights Out	multiplication facts	2–4	rhyming words, time, upper-/lowercase letters	108
What Time Is It?	time to the quarter hour	2–3		109
Mozart By Moonlight	fractions	1–3	categorization, vowel combinations, math fact families	110
Pretty In Pink	odd/even numbers	1–2	vowels, upper-/lowercase letters, hard-/soft-g	111
Right Down The Middle!	subtraction	2–3	math sentences	112
Ozzie Ostrich	numbers/sets	K–1	initial consonants	113
Shell It Out!	money	1–2	blends, fractions, abbreviations	114
Great Snakes Alive!	greater than/less than	1–3	true/false, spelling, vowels	115
Raining Cats And Dogs	mixed math	2–3		116
Dandy Doubleheader	addition facts	1–2	place value, syllabication, nouns/verbs	117
Thunder And Lightning	numbers/sets	K–1		118
'Twas The Night Before…	number sequence	K–1	alphabetical order, word order in sentences, counting	119
Giggle Boxes	shapes	K–1	colors/color words, categorization	120
Fickle Pickles	place value to 1000s	2–4		121
Coupon Sense	money/charts	3–4		122
Counting Sheep	counting	K–1		123
Animal Snackers	subtraction	2–3	vowels, nouns/verbs, hard-/soft-c	124
Too Many Tickets	money	2–3	antonyms, math facts, colors/color words, abbreviations	125
Busy Math Bees	number sequence	K–1	counting by 2s, 3s, 5s	126
Pocket Change	addition	2–3	complete sentences, odd/even, cities/states, upper-/lowercase letters	127
Sock Drawer	mixed math	2–4		128
Spooky Sale	addition/subtraction of money	2–4		129

Monster Mouth

This merry monster has an appetite for correct subtraction facts. Draw a zigzagged mouth line approximately two inches from the folded edge of a file folder. Cut along this line (see Step 1); then staple the ends of the mouth to the sides of the folder to form a pocket (see Step 2). Draw the rest of the monster's head on the folder and cut around the edges (see Step 2). Label cut-out cookies (or the reproducible cookie cards on page 185) with correct and incorrect subtraction facts. Students feed the hungry beast only cookies with correct facts.

Label additional cookies with fact/opinion statements, upper-/lowercase letters, hard-/soft-*c* words, and synonym/antonym word pairs.

Feed the monster only the cookies with correct math facts.

MONSTER MOUTH

8-3=5

Step 1

Step 2

Staple sides.

12-6=7

Drumstick Drill

Real toothpicks make the beat of this drummer different and fun! Attach a pocket to the back of the folder to store 55 toothpicks. Students count out the correct number of toothpicks for each drum.

Fancy Pants

Match the shapes and turn this clown's plain trousers into fancy pants! Cut shapes to match those on the folder from construction paper, wallpaper, or fabric. Laminate the cutouts if desired before storing them in a pocket inside the folder.

Make the clown's pants fancy. Place the matching pieces on the clown.

107

Lights Out

Multiplication time, and the lights are out! Label a set of cards (the same size as the windows inside the folder) with answers to the multiplication problems. Cut out the cards; then color the back of each with a black marker or crayon. Store the cards in a pocket on the back of the folder. After placing each card on the correct window, the student flips the cards over so all the "lights" will go out.

Try this format for matching rhyming words, digital times/clock faces, or upper-/lowercase letters.

What Time Is It?

The simple appeal of this hands-on file folder is timeless! Attach poster board hands to the clock with a brad. When you're ready for a change, just paste a piece of paper labeled with new times over the old directions.

What time is it?
Show these times
on the clock:

9:45	11:15
7:30	6:30
3:45	10:00
12:00	1:30
2:15	4:00
5:30	8:00

Mozart By Moonlight

These feline fiddlers are playing a fraction tune that will be music to your students' ears! Label cut-out cards with fraction pictures. Store the cards in a pocket on the back of the folder. Laminate the cards and folder if desired.

Adapt this folder to other skills by labeling the trash cans with categories, vowel combinations, or math fact families. Make cards to match.

Pretty In Pink

Helping Ms. Porcupine primp will be so much fun students won't notice that they're learning! Copy the artwork and laminate. Add the directions using a permanent marker. Duplicate several copies of the bow card patterns on page 186. Program the cards with even and odd numbers. Laminate the cards and store them in a pocket on the back of the folder.

For other uses, program bow cards with long-/short-vowel words, upper-/lowercase letters, or hard-/soft-*g* words.

Put only even-numbered bows on the porcupine.

Porcupine Beauty Cream

Net. Wt. 1.3 oz.

Pretty in Pink

Right Down The Middle!

Here's some mathematics magic! Label cut-out cards with incorrect and correct subtraction equations for students to sort. Code the backs of the cards for self-checking as shown. Store the cards in a pocket on the back of the folder.

To vary, write an operation sign (+, −, x, or ÷) on each half of the table. Label the cards with math facts, omitting the signs.

Place each card on the correct box.
Turn the cards over to check.

$$\begin{array}{r} 37 \\ -15 \\ \hline 23 \end{array}$$

I

Correct

Incorrect

Ozzie Ostrich

Younger students will enjoy helping Ozzie Ostrich identify her family of eggs. Use a stamp pad and the eraser on a new pencil to make dot patterns on the eggs in the folder (or use the reproducible dot sets on page 171). Duplicate five copies of the egg patterns on page 187 on construction paper. Label the cut-out eggs with numerals before laminating and cutting them out. Store the egg cutouts in a pocket on the back of the folder.

To change this folder to a reading activity, program the folder eggs and egg cutouts with picture words and letters of the alphabet.

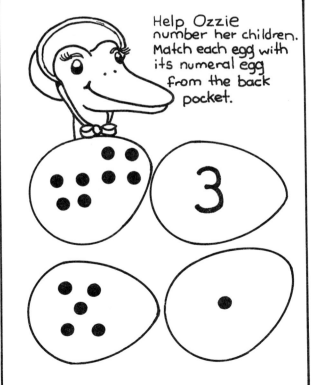

Help Ozzie number her children. Match each egg with its numeral egg from the back pocket.

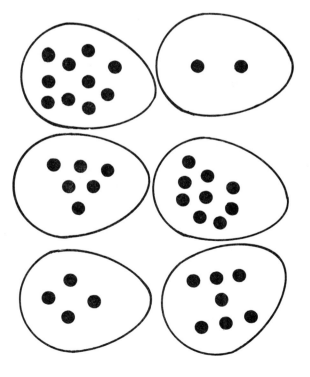

113

Shell It Out!

A set of rubber stamps will help speed up construction of this coin-counting activity. Stamp coin amounts on cut-out seashells (patterns on page 187), or use the reproducible coins on pages 165–167. Label the backs of the shells with the correct amounts. Store the cutouts in a pocket on the back of the folder.

Use this seashell theme for other skills: blends and picture words, fractions and pictures, or words and their abbreviations.

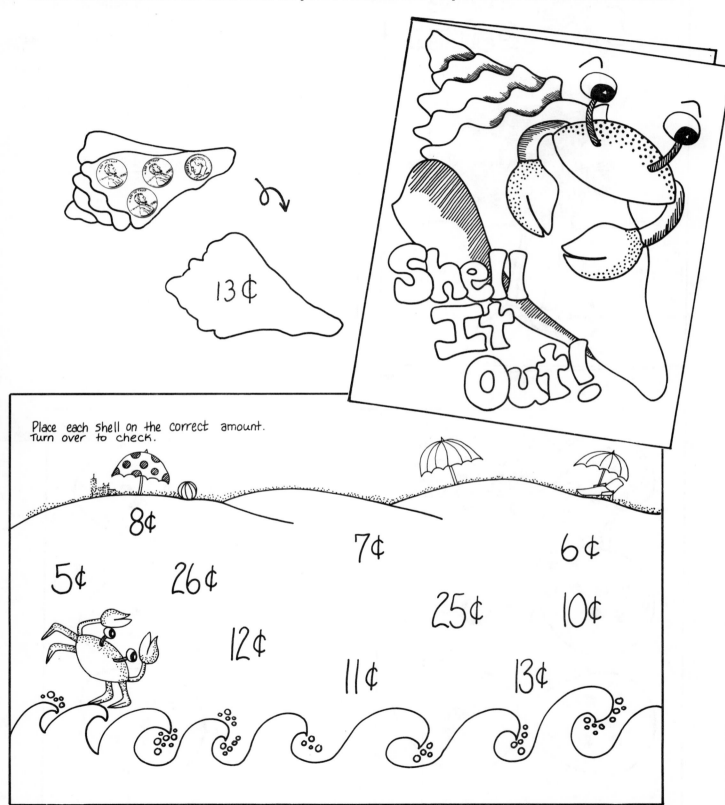

Place each shell on the correct amount. Turn over to check.

8¢

5¢   26¢   7¢   6¢

25¢   10¢

12¢

11¢   13¢

13¢

Great Snakes Alive!

Reinforce basic numeration skills with this greater than/less than drill. Attach two labeled pockets inside the folder (see illustration). Label a set of cut-out cards as shown and store them in a pocket on the back of the folder.

As an alternative, label cards with true/false statements, correct/incorrect spelling words, even/odd numbers, or long-/short-vowel words. Change the pockets to match.

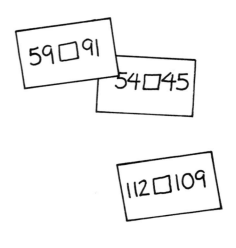

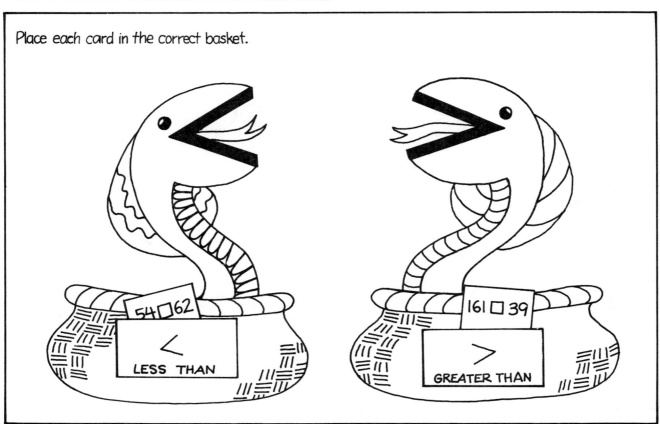

Place each card in the correct basket.

Raining Cats And Dogs

Get caught in a cat and dog downpour, and improve math skills! Copy the artwork; then use three or four different colors of markers or crayons to color the cats and dogs. Label cut-out cards with various math tasks. Store the cards and an answer key in a pocket attached to the folder.

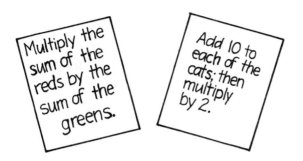

©1991 The Education Center, Inc.

Dandy Doubleheader

Addition batting averages will go up with this sorting review! Duplicate several copies of the baseball patterns on page 187 on white construction paper. Label the baseballs with correct and incorrect addition facts; then laminate and cut them out. Attach two labeled pockets inside the folder as shown.

This center is also dandy for other sorting skills: place value, syllabication, hard-/soft-*c* words, and nouns/verbs.

Thunder And Lightning

April showers bring lots of counting practice! On yellow construction paper, duplicate several copies of the lightning bolt patterns on page 188. Label each bolt with a number word; then laminate and cut out. Use a permanent marker to program the backs of the bolts for self-checking. Store the bolts in a pocket on the back of the folder.

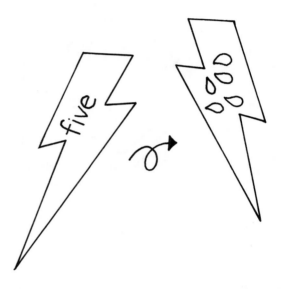

Count the raindrops under each thundercloud. Place the matching lightning bolt on the cloud.

'Twas The Night Before…

There's nothing like a cozy fire to warm up sequencing skills! Duplicate several copies of the stocking patterns on page 188. Label each stocking with a number; then laminate and cut out. Store the stockings in a pocket on the back of the folder.

Use this fireplace for any activity involving sequencing: counting, word order in a sentence, alphabet, alphabetical order of words. Change the directions and prepare new sets of stocking cutouts.

"The stockings were hung by the chimney with care."
Place these stockings in the correct order to count by 2s.

Giggle Boxes

Shape discrimination has never been so much fun! Cut out shapes from construction paper to match those shown on the jack-in-the-boxes. Store the pieces in a pocket on the back of the folder.

To vary, have students match pieces cut from wallpaper samples or textured fabric. Or label the jack-in-the-boxes and cutouts with colors/color words or categories/pictures.

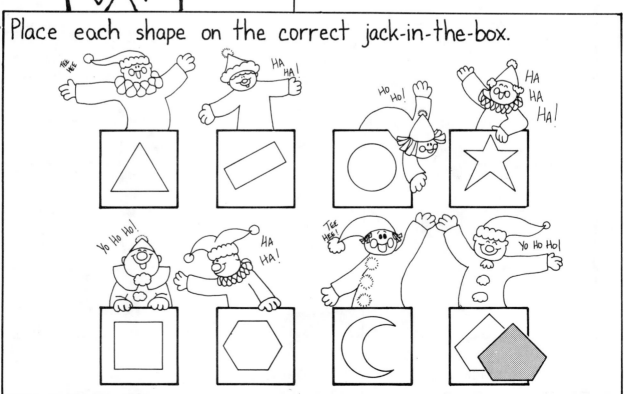

Place each shape on the correct jack-in-the-box.

Fickle Pickles

Take a bite out of place value skills with the help of these fickle pickles! On green construction paper, duplicate several copies of the pickle cards on page 188. Label each card with a number, underlining one digit of the number. Laminate and cut out the cards. Code the backs of the cards with color dots that correspond to the colors of the jar labels. Store the cards in a pocket glued to the folder as shown.

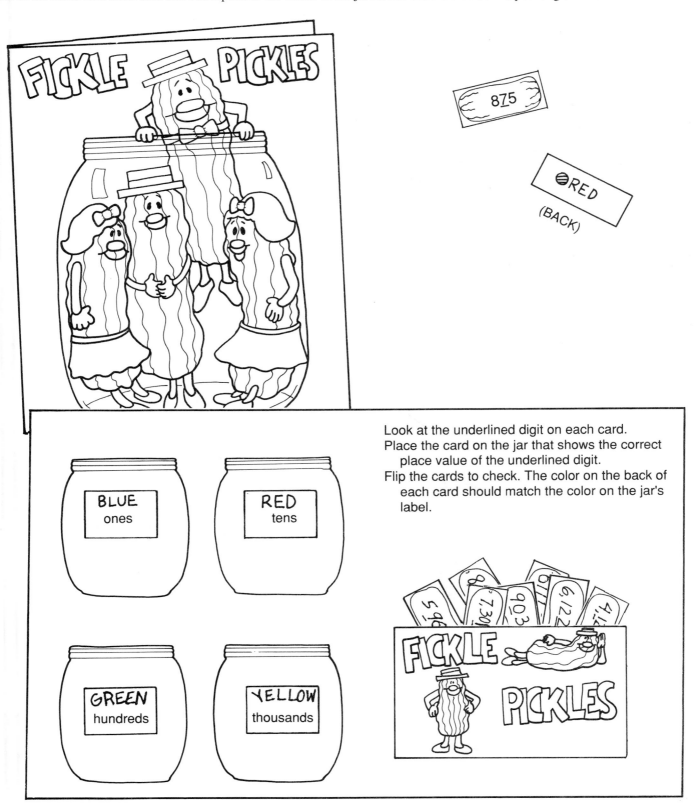

Look at the underlined digit on each card.
Place the card on the jar that shows the correct place value of the underlined digit.
Flip the cards to check. The color on the back of each card should match the color on the jar's label.

Coupon Sense

With a "clip, clip" here and a "clip, clip" there, you can make this money skills folder in no time! Have students bring in money-saving coupons they have cut from newspapers or magazines. Label several index cards with five or six of the items found on the coupons, making sure that each card is different. Store the cards and the coupons in pockets attached to the inside of the folder.

Item Cards

Coupons

CASH COUPONS

SAMPLE CHART

Item	Price	Coupon Value	Actual Cost
Wheaties	$ .65	$ .10	$ .55
Downy	$ .83	$ .10	$ .73

DIRECTIONS:
1. Draw an item card from the top pocket.
2. Make a chart like the example above on your paper. Pull out the coupons to fill in your chart.
3. Total your actual cost.
4. What would the total cost be without the coupons?
5. How much was saved?

Counting Sheep

Your youngsters will love the counting practice these woolly friends provide. On white construction paper, duplicate several copies of the sheep patterns on page 189. Laminate the sheep, if desired, before cutting them out. Add a spinner to the folder. Store the sheep cutouts in a pocket on the back of the folder.

Spin. Count out the correct number of sheep.

Animal Snackers

Munch on subtraction problems with this pocket activity. Trim the front of the folder as shown (Step 1) and staple the sides to form a pocket (Step 2). Duplicate several copies of the cookie card patterns on page 185; then label them with correct and incorrect subtraction equations. Laminate the cards if desired. After cutting the cards apart, store them in the pocket.

To vary, label the cookie cards with long-/short-vowel words, nouns/verbs, or hard-/soft-*c* words.

©1991 The Education Center, Inc.

Too Many Tickets

Here's just the ticket for practicing money skills! Use a rubber stamp set (or the reproducible coin patterns on pages 165–167) to label cut-out tickets with money amounts to match those on the folder. Cut out the tickets; then code the backs for self-checking. Store the tickets in a pocket attached to the back of the folder.

Use this format for other matching activities: antonyms, math facts/answers, colors/color words, words/abbreviations, or synonyms.

Match the amounts.
Look on the backs of the cards to check.

20¢ ○ 22¢ ○ 15¢

27¢ ○ 17¢ ○ 30¢

21¢ ○ 12¢ ○ 26¢

Busy Math Bees

This folder is buzzing with number-sequence drill. Draw the beehive and glue a storage pocket on its base. Number cut-out bees (patterns on page 189) from one to 20, and place them in the pocket.

To increase the difficulty, make additional sets of bees for counting by 2's, 3's, or 5's.

Pocket Change

To make this fun pocket folder, see the illustrations on page 124. Write correct and incorrect addition sentences on play money or copies of the pattern below. Students place only correct equations in the pocket.

Program additional sets of play money with complete/incomplete sentences, even/odd numbers, cities/states, or upper-/lowercase letters.

Pattern

Sock Drawer

Sock it to 'em with a drawer full of multiplication problems. Cut a slit along the dotted line and insert a paper clip. Label several cut-out cards with directions (see example); then clip one card onto the center. Store the extra cards and an answer key in a pocket on the back of the folder.

Spooky Sale

Go on a ghostly spending spree! Add a spinner to the wheel. Students spin an amount and list the items they can buy.

Spin an amount.
Make a list of all the items
you can buy.
Add up your total.
Be sure you don't spend
more than the amount
you spun!

129

Skillboards

Skillboards are made from 17" x 22" sheets of white poster board. To transfer the illustration onto the poster board, use an opaque projector. Or trace the illustration on a piece of acetate; then use an overhead projector to project the tracing onto a sheet of poster board taped to the wall.

Most of the Skillboards require additional game pieces, which you can either store in a pocket on the center or in a separate box or envelope. To make storage pockets long-lasting, laminate them separately and attach them to the center with plastic tape.

Look at all the centers, not just those pertaining to the skill or grade level of your students. Almost every Skillboard shown is adaptable to the interests and needs of your class.

Name	Skill	Grade	Variations	Page
One Potato, Two Potato	sets/numbers/number words	K–1	vowel combination *ea*, plurals, contractions	131
Pied Piper Parade	number sequence	K–1	alphabet sequence, days of the week, alphabetical order	132
Kneepad Know-how	time to the half hour	1–2	digraphs, states/capitals, numbers/number words, initial consonants	133
Yellow Brick Road	number recognition	K–1		134
Secondhand Rose	multiplication facts	2–4	addition, subtraction	135
Catch A Number	number chart	K–1		136
Band-Aid Boo-boos	addition facts	1–2	equivalent measurements, antonyms, states/capitals, contractions	137
Inspector Mooseau	sets/numbers/number words	K–1		138
Duck!	counting	K–1	vowels	139
Place Value Spinner	place value	1–3		140
Frosty And Drippy	division facts	2–4	complete sentences, spelling, contractions/possessives	141
Fruit Cart	addition/subtraction	1–3	vowels, money, nouns/verbs, true/false	142
Night Lights	addition facts	1–2	abbreviations, subtraction, time	143
Tweety's Totals	mixed math	1–3		144
Undercover Cats	money	2–4		145
Time To Wake Up!	greater than/less than	1–3	true/false, math facts, cause/effect, odd/even	146
Catch A Falling Star	counting	K–1		147
Dottie's Diner	subtraction facts	1–2	addition, multiplication	148
Balancing Bear	time to ten minutes	2–4	initial consonants, rhyming words/pictures, synonyms	149
Matador Madness	multiplication facts	2–4	addition, subtraction	150
Seymour Seal	sets/numbers/number words	K–1	synonyms, rhyming words	151
Banana Boat Float	place value to 1000s	2–3	ending punctuation, categorization	152
Neck And Neck	addition facts	1–2	multiplication, compound words	153
Bobbing For Apples	division facts	3–4	short vowels, homonyms, time	154
Bedtime For Polly's Puppies	numbers/sets	K–1	colors/color words, math facts, homonyms	155
Jungle Juggler	writing math equations	1–3		156
Secret Signs	shapes	K–1		157
Great Gators	greater than/less than	1–2	fractions, sets	158
This Little Piggy	money	1–2	initial consonants, blends, vocabulary, contractions	159
Midnight Mousequerade	fractions	1–2	addition, rhyming words/pictures	160
Calico Critters	subtraction facts	1–2	punctuation, spelling, addition	161

One Potato, Two Potato

Follow these ants to number mastery! Complete the Skillboard and laminate. Cut out 30 potato shapes (patterns on page 190). Label ten of them with number words, ten with numbers, and ten with dot sets (patterns on pages 171–175). Glue a pocket on the back for storage.

Adapt the activity to other three-part matching skills: sounds of *ea*, plural endings, or contractions.

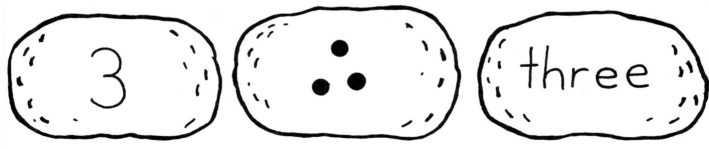

Pied Piper Parade

This versatile sequencing center takes its theme from a favorite story. Label mice cards (patterns on page 189) with numbers to place in correct order. Attach a pocket on the Skillboard to store the cards.

Young students can also order alphabet letters or days of the week, while older students can brush up on alphabetizing skills.

©1991 The Education Center, Inc.

Kneepad Know-how

Get knee-deep in math practice with this Skillboard on telling time. Cut slits along the dotted lines and insert paper clips. Duplicate the blank clock cards on page 163; then add clock hands to each card. Label another, blank set of cards with digital times to match the clock cards. Color-code the backs of the cards for easy self-checking. Store the cards in a pocket on the back of the Skillboard.

Adapt this activity to any matching skill: states/capitals, digraphs/missing-digraph words, numbers/number words, or pictures/initial consonants.

Yellow Brick Road

Follow this golden path to improved numeration skills! Label a set of cut-out cards with directions such as the ones shown. Provide two to four game markers. Store the markers and the cards in a pocket on the back of the Skillboard.

Directions for two to four players:
1. Place the cards facedown on the board.
2. In turn, draw a card and move to the number indicated.
3. If you draw a "Back to..." card, move back to the number indicated.
4. The first to reach the Emerald City wins!

Place cards here.

Go to 5.

Back to 1.

Back to 3.

Go to 6.

Secondhand Rose

She may not be on the Best-dressed List, but Secondhand Rose's math practice is always in style. Label several self-sticking dots with numbers; then press them onto Rose's coat. Cut a slit along the dotted line and insert a paper clip. Attach a cut-out card labeled with a task as shown.

For younger students, prepare addition and subtraction task cards. Write larger numbers on the dots to give older students more challenging practice.

Catch A Number

Here's an interesting way to call attention to a number. Make a number chart as shown. Trace the baseball catcher's mitt pattern on page 190 onto poster board, and cut it out. Use an X-acto knife to cut out a square (equal to one of your chart's number squares) in the middle of the mitt.

Hold the mitt over the number you want your students to name, add, subtract, multiply, etc. Or have students tell you what number comes before or after the number displayed.

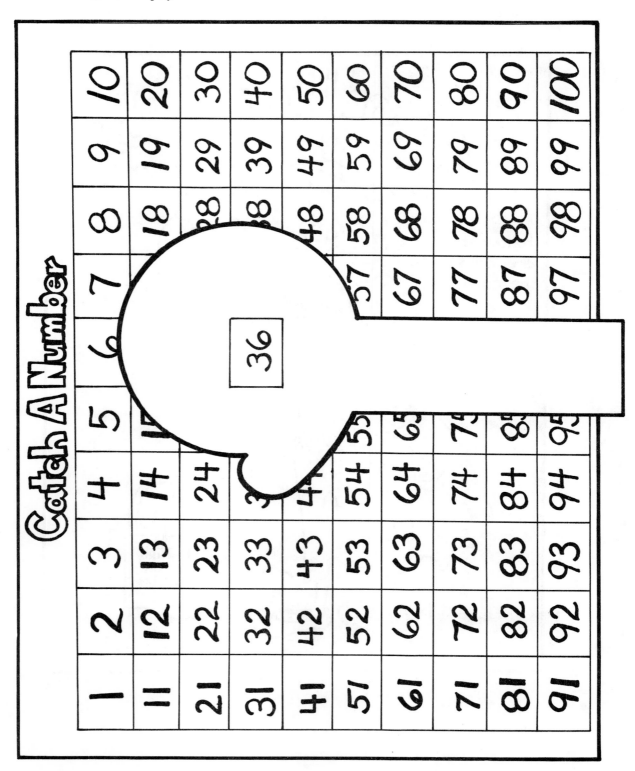

©1991 The Education Center, Inc.

Band-Aid Boo-boos

Addition facts will stick with your children when they use this Skillboard! Copy the artwork onto poster board and laminate. Label small, self-sticking dots with math problems; then apply them to the giraffe. On small Band-Aids, write the answers to the problems. Adhere the Band-Aids to the Skillboard as shown. Students cover up each addition problem with the correct Band-Aid. When you're ready for a change, simply remove the dots and Band-Aids, and replace them with new ones.

Use this same technique for antonyms, equivalent measurements, states/capitals, or contractions/word pairs.

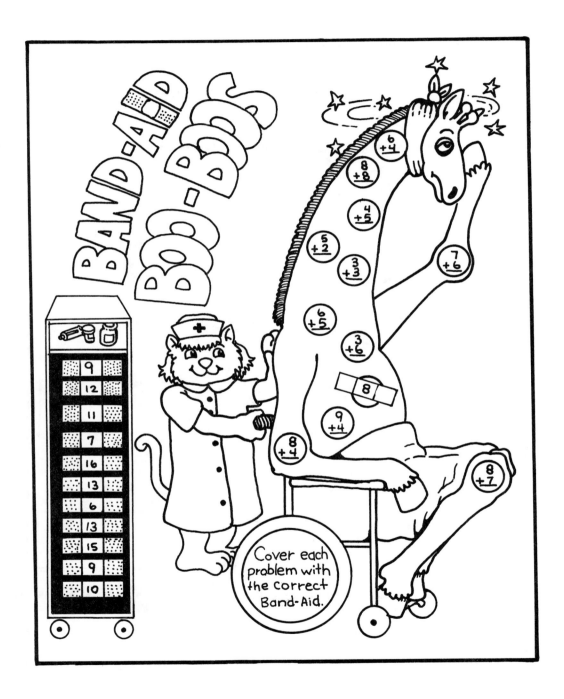

Inspector Mooseau

Inspector Mooseau is hot on the trail of numeration drill! Cut out two different colors of cards. Label one set with numbers and the other with matching sets. Cut out ten circles and label them with number words. (See the reproducible patterns for sets, numbers, and number words on pages 171–175.) Cut slits along the dotted lines and insert paper clips. Attach two pockets to the Skillboard as shown.

Clip one number word circle onto the magnifying glass. Have students locate the matching set and numeral cards and clip them to the center.

Duck!

You'll hear chuckles as students count to complete this picture. Attach a spinner to the number wheel and make a slit over the ball bucket. On the back of the Skillboard, glue a paper pocket directly under the slit. Duplicate the baseball patterns on page 187 on construction paper and cut them out. Store them in the ball bucket pocket.

To use this format for a word attack activity, label the wheel with vowels and the baseball with words to sort.

Place Value Spinner

Who will be the winner of Place Value Spinner? Attach six pockets to the Skillboard as shown. Cut out 200–250 small, paper "tickets" and store them with several paper clips in a pocket on the back of the Skillboard. Attach a spinner to the turtle's wheel. As your students progress, update the game by adding "hundreds" pockets and changing the point values on the spinner.

140

Frosty And Drippy

A pair of snowmen are perfect helpers for students who need to practice division facts. Label cut-out cards with correct and incorrect division facts. Code the backs of the cards for self-checking; then store them in a pocket attached to the back of the Skillboard.

Use Frosty and Drippy to give students practice in sorting incomplete/complete sentences, incorrect/correct spelling words, or contractions/possessives.

Place correct cards on Frosty.
Place incorrect cards on Drippy.
Turn the cards over to check.

Fruit Cart

Don't upset this fruit basket—it's loaded with practice in addition and subtraction! Label the signs on the cart as shown. On cut-out cards, write math equations that are missing either the + or – sign. Store the cards in a pocket on the back of the Skillboard. Students place each card on the correct sign on the fruit cart.

Relabel the signs and make additional card sets labeled with long-/short-vowel words, less-than/more-than 50 cents coin amounts, nouns/verbs, or true/false statements.

©1991 The Education Center, Inc.

Night Lights

Brighten up addition drill with these funny fireflies. Cut out bulbs (patterns on page 191) from poster board and label with addition facts. Store the bulbs in a pocket on the front of the poster. If you wish to add a self-correcting feature, color each lightning bug a different color and put a dot of that same color on the back of the matching bulb.

To vary, have these bright bugs provide practice with time, abbreviations, or subtraction facts.

Tweety's Totals

The colors on this chilly chap's cap are the key to multilevel math drill. Write tasks involving different math operations on cut-out cards (see examples). Store the cards in a pocket attached to the back of the Skillboard.

Use Tweety's Totals with older students by labeling the cap with larger numbers, decimal numbers, or fractions.

Subtract the total of the numbers on the green stripes from the total on the blue stripes.

Add 15 to each odd number.

Add 2 to each number.

144

Undercover Cats

Students will spy many different combinations of coins and dollar bills to equal the amount shown at the top of this wall. Cut a slit where indicated and add a paper clip. Use a rubber stamp to label about 40 cut-out cards with single coins (or use the reproducible coin cards on pages 165–167). Draw a dollar bill on about five cut-out cards. Label several task cards with money amounts; then insert one in the paper clip. Change this task card frequently. Store all of the cards in a pocket on the back of the center.

Time To Wake Up!

Watch out for these two sleepwalkers on a collision course with < and > practice! Use the patterns on page 191 to make 20 cards. Label each with a number sentence, omitting the < or > sign. To make the cards self-checking, code the backs with answers. Add a pocket on the back of the center to store the cards.

To get more use from this Skillboard, reprogram it and make new cards for sorting true/false statements, incorrect/correct math equations, cause/effect statements, or even/odd numbers.

Catch A Falling Star

Add some sparkle to math time with these falling stars. Complete the artwork, laminate, and add a spinner in the center of the number wheel. Use the patterns on page 177 to make ten star cutouts. To store the stars, cut a slit over the star bucket and glue a pocket on the back of the Skillboard under the slit.

Dottie's Diner

These two number wheels provide almost endless math practice. Laminate the Skillboard; then add a spinner to each wheel. Fasten the spinners loosely so they will spin freely. Ask students to spin and subtract the smaller number from the larger.

To vary the activity, have students write addition word problems using the numbers or multiply.

Balancing Bear

Balancing Bear has all the time in the world to help students practice this important skill! Cut out circles the size of those on the Skillboard from two colors of construction paper. Label circles of one color with digital times. On the other circles, glue duplicated copies of the blank clock faces on page 163. Add hands to match the digital times on the other circles. Store all of the circles in a pocket on the back of the Skillboard. Have students place matching circles on Balancing Bear's dumbbell.

To vary, program cut-out circles with pictures/final consonants, rhyming words or pictures, states/capitals, math facts/answers, or synonyms.

Matador Madness

Here's a Skillboard that's packed with multiplication drill! Attach two spinners to the number wheels as shown. Store a multiplication table (to use as an answer key) in a pocket on the back of the Skillboard.

Have younger students add the two numbers spun or subtract the smaller number from the larger one.

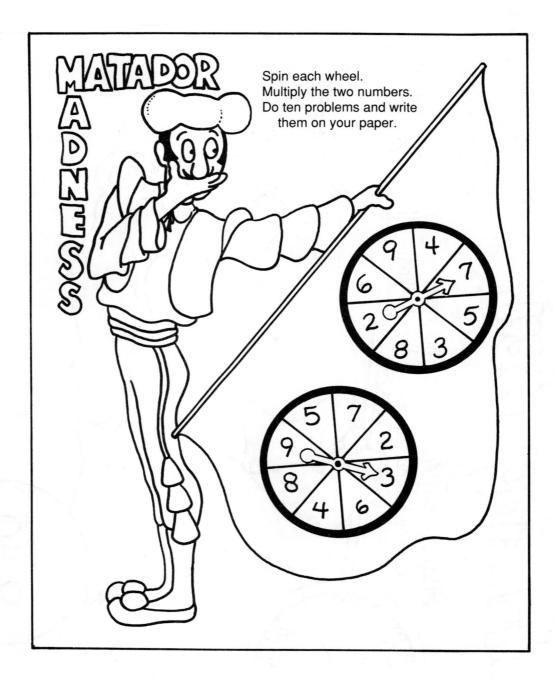

Spin each wheel.
Multiply the two numbers.
Do ten problems and write
them on your paper.

Seymour Seal

Seymour does a balancing act to help your students with number recognition skills. Use the patterns on page 191 to make 30 beach ball cutouts. Label ten cutouts with numerals 1–10, ten with matching sets, and ten with matching number words (or use the reproducible patterns on pages 171–175). Store the balls in a pocket on the back of the Skillboard.

Let Seymour balance additional beach balls labeled with synonyms or rhyming words.

Give Seymour the matching beach balls.

Banana Boat Float

Make a banana split that's full of place value review! Label cut-out cards with two-, three-, and four-digit numbers. Underline one digit in each number. Cut slits along the dotted lines on the scoops and insert paper clips. Add a pocket on the back of the Skillboard to store the cards.

For a variation, change the labels on the scoops to ending punctuation marks, </>/= signs, or categories. Make new sets of matching cards.

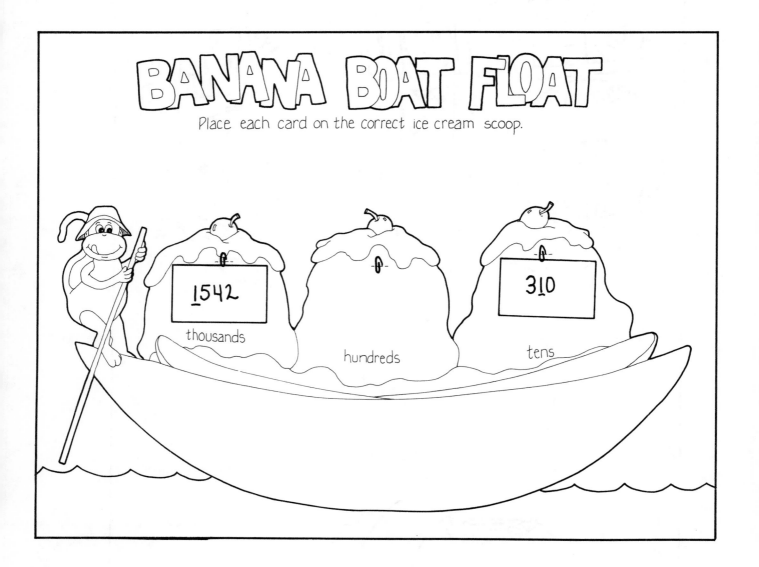

152

Neck And Neck

Don't get all tied up with addition practice—these birds will do the work for you! Attach a spinner to each number wheel. Store an answer key in a pocket attached to the back of the Skillboard.

Neck And Neck is also good for drilling multiplication facts. Or write words on the wheels; then have students spin to form compound words.

153

Bobbing For Apples

An apple a day keeps poor math skills away! Duplicate a supply of the apple patterns on page 192. Label each apple with a division fact. Cut slits on the Skillboard and insert the apples as shown. Make several sets of apples labeled with other math facts so that the center can be changed quickly and easily.

Use this format for practicing other skills such as long or short vowels, homonyms, ending punctuation, or time.

154

Bedtime For Polly's Puppies

Help Polly put her puppies to bed while practicing sets. Use the patterns on page 192 to make 10 puppy cutouts. Label the puppies with dot sets. Store the puppies in a pocket that has been glued on the front of the Skillboard.

Polly's puppies are also great for matching colors/color words, math facts/answers, or homonyms.

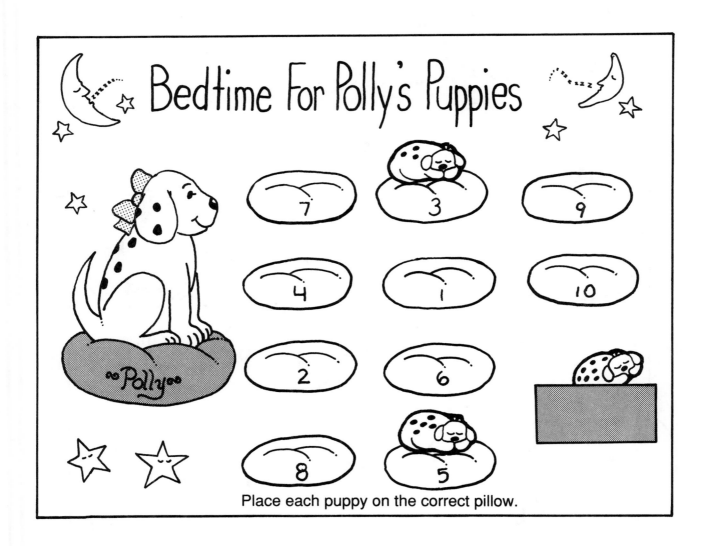

Jungle Juggler

This jungle juggler has his hands full of math practice! Cut slits along the dotted lines and insert paper clips. Cut out a supply of circles from colorful construction paper. Write math symbols and numbers on the circles; then have students clip them to the board to make math equations as shown. Store the circles in a pocket attached to the back of the Skillboard.

Clip balls to the board to make math equations. Write the equations on your paper.

Secret Signs

With a wave of his magic wand, this wise wizard is ready to help youngsters identify basic shapes. Cut out shapes to match those on the Skillboard from fabric, wallpaper, or construction paper. Store the cutouts in a pocket on the back of the Skillboard. To extend the activity, ask students to give the name of each shape as they find a match.

Great Gators

Math symbols masquerade as alligator jaws on this Skillboard. Cut slits along the dotted lines and insert paper clips. Label a set of cut-out cards with numbers. Store the cards in a pocket on the back of the Skillboard.

Make Great Gators more appropriate for older students by supplying cards labeled with fractions or decimals. For younger students, draw dot sets on the cards (or use the reproducible dot set cards on page 171).

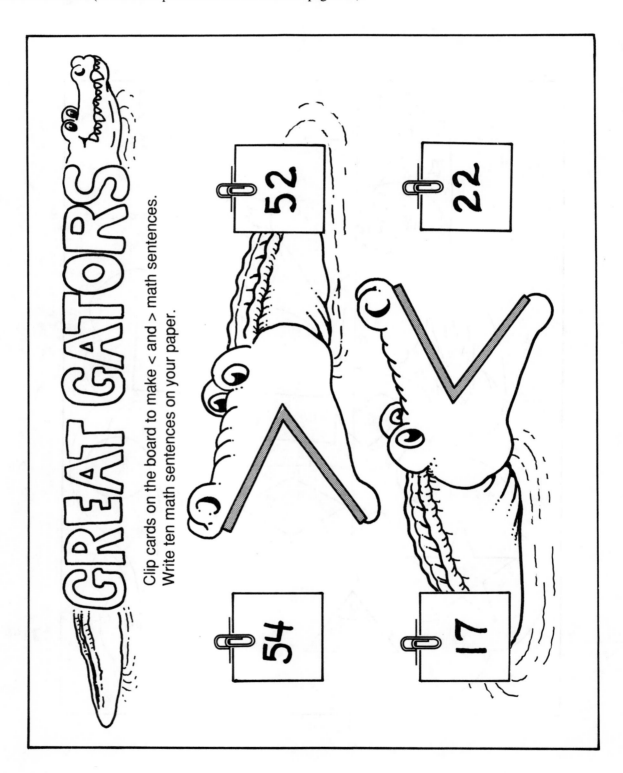

This Little Piggy

Use a rubber stamp set or the reproducible coin patterns on pages 165–167 to make the cards for this appealing activity. Cut a slit across the top of each piggy bank. On cut-out cards, stamp various coin groups. Store the cards in a pocket on the back of the Skillboard. Use these piggy banks with other skills such as initial consonants, blends, vocabulary, or contractions.

Midnight Mousequerade

Are your students tired of drab fractions practice? Then Midnight Mousequerade is just what they need. On cut-out cards, draw illustrations of the Skillboard's fractions. Mount the cards on tagboard. Laminate and cut them out. Code the backs of the cards for self-checking. Attach a pocket to the back of the center to store the cards.

This center is so appealing you're going to want to use it in several different ways. For math fact practice, program each balloon with a sum. Provide matching math problem cards which are coded for self-checking. For rhyming practice, program each balloon with a word. Provide picture-word cards which are coded for self-checking.

Calico Critters

There's nothing like a cuddly friend to help you practice subtraction facts! Label cut-out cards with correct and incorrect subtraction problems. Store the cards in a pocket attached to the front of the Skillboard.

Since the directions are open, it's a snap to reprogram this activity for other skills. Make new cards labeled with correct/incorrect spelling words, correctly/incorrectly punctuated sentences, or correct/incorrect addition facts.

(continued on next page)

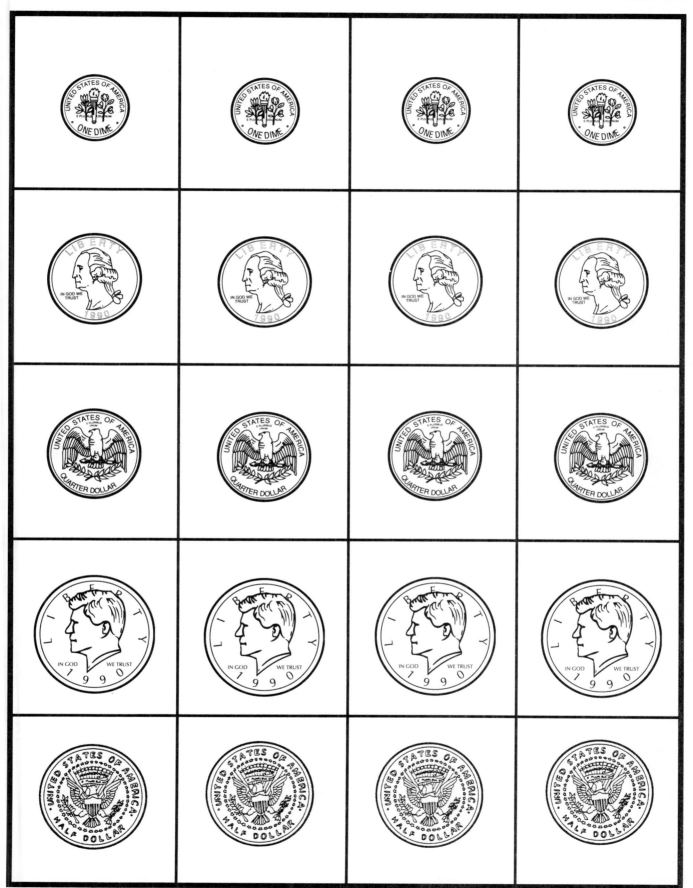

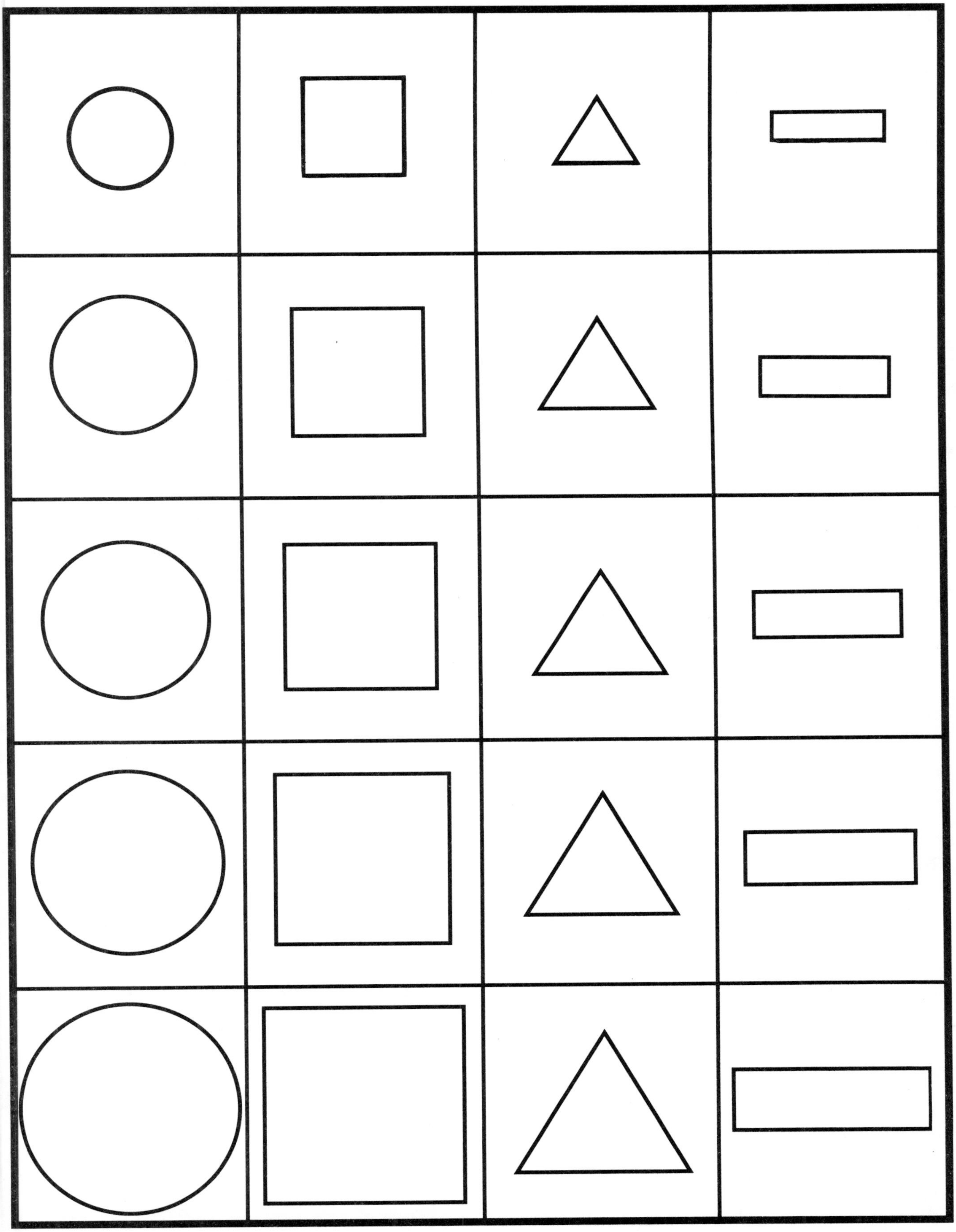

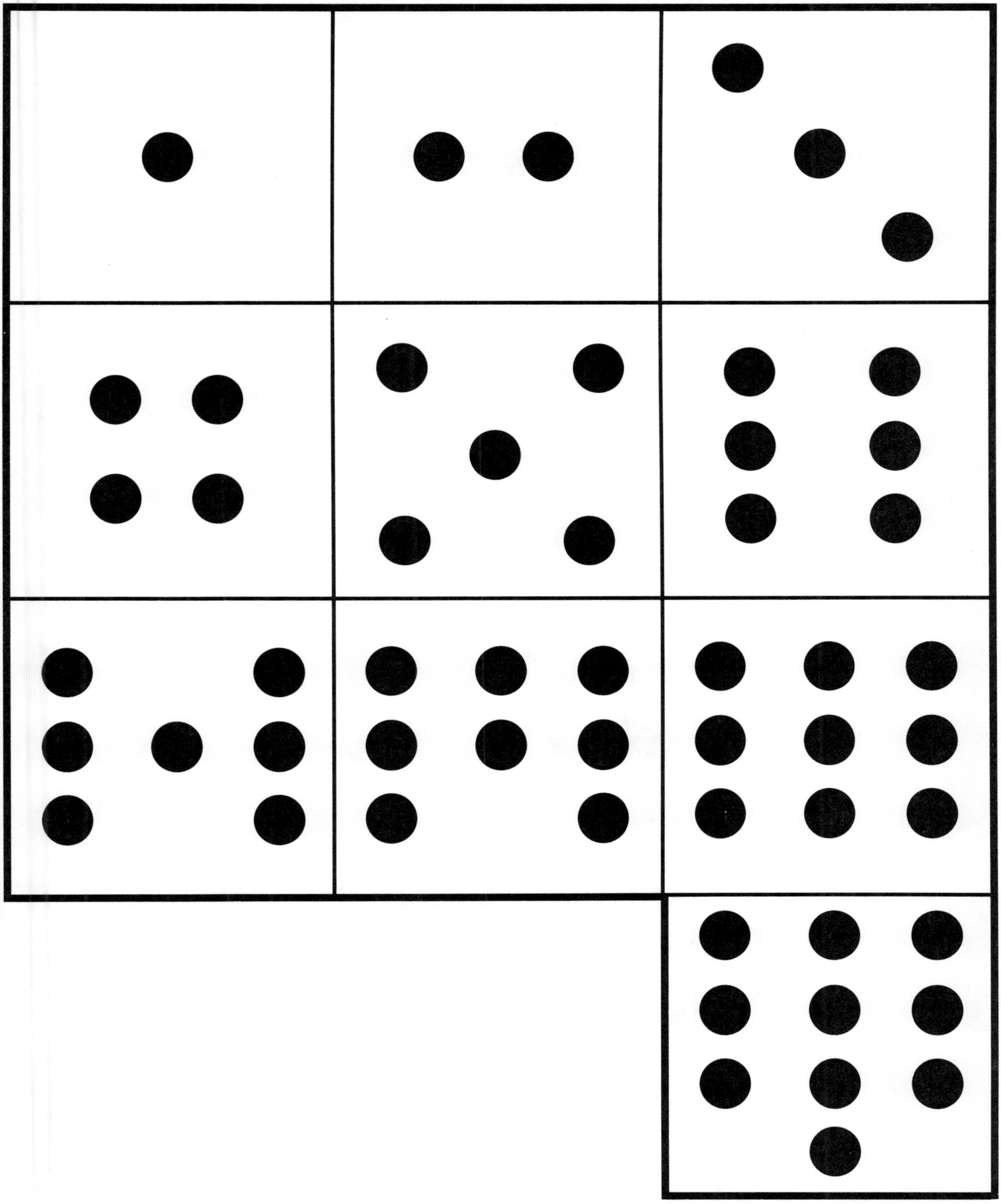

1	2	3
4	5	6
7	8	9
		10

one	two	three
four	five	six
seven	eight	nine
		ten

Patterns

Use the newspaper card patterns with the "Paper Boys" Cut-out on page 8.

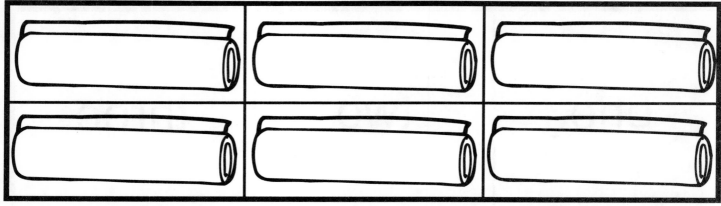

Enlarge the damsel-in-distress pattern and use it with the "Monster Grip" Cut-out on page 14.

Whew! Saved!

Use the mitten pattern with the "A Show Of Hands" Cut-out on page 12.

Use the ice-cream scoop patterns with the "Sugar Shack" Cut-out on page 15.

Use the star patterns with the "Stars And Stripes" Cut-out on page 18, the "Ship Shapes" Cut-out on page 37, and the "Catch A Falling Star" Skillboard on page 147.

Use the mouse pattern with the "The Big Cheese" Cut-out on page 19.

Enlarge the Cannonball Jones pattern to use with the "Cannonball Jones" Cut-out on page 20.

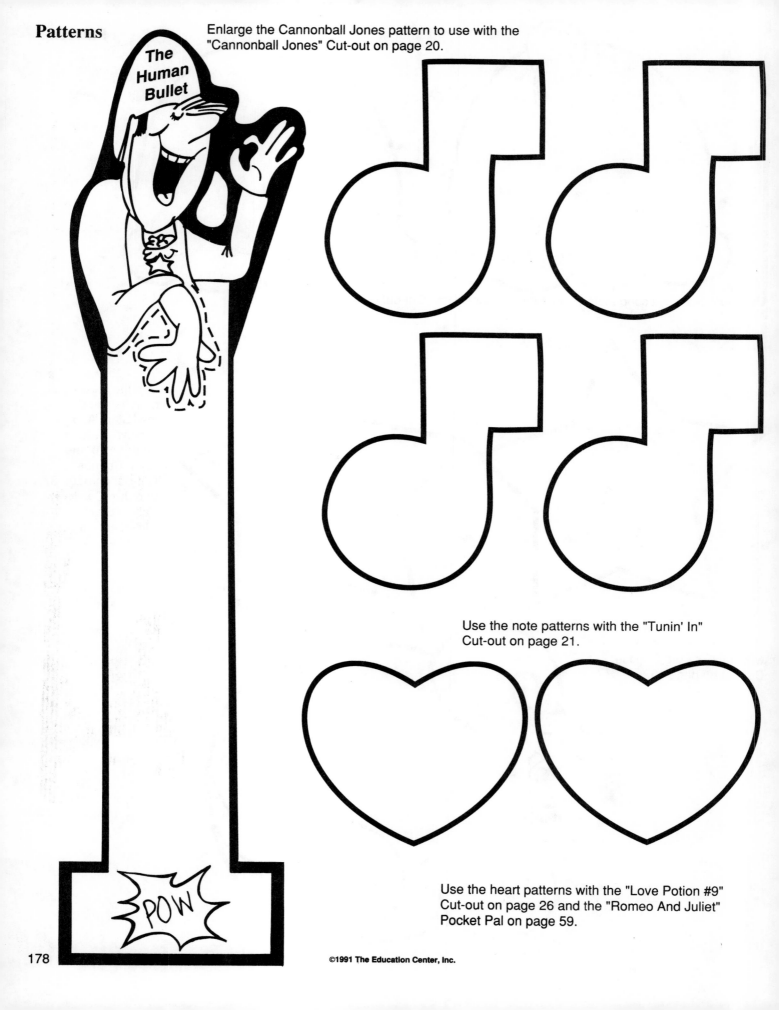

The Human Bullet

POW

Use the note patterns with the "Tunin' In" Cut-out on page 21.

Use the heart patterns with the "Love Potion #9" Cut-out on page 26 and the "Romeo And Juliet" Pocket Pal on page 59.

Use the fish card patterns with the "Balancing Buddies"
Cut-out on page 30.

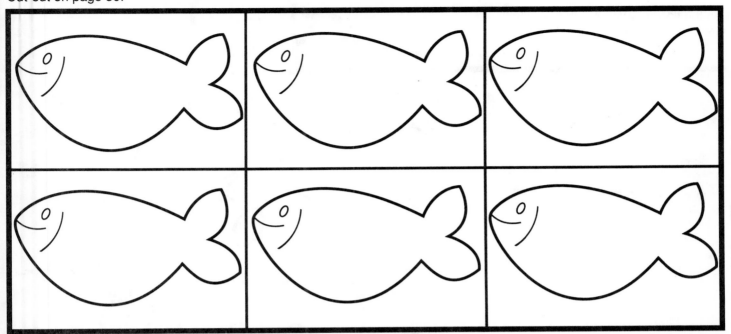

Use the dolphin pattern
with the "Dolphin Delight"
Cut-out on page 49.

Use the teddy bear
patterns with the
"Animal Cookies"
Cut-out on page 50.

Patterns

Use the flower patterns with the
"Green Thumb" Cut-out on page 41.

Use the dragon card patterns with the "Hide-and-Seek"
Pocket Pal on page 53.

Use the bed, blanket, and
bug patterns with the
"Snuggle Buggles" Pocket Pal
on page 66.

Patterns

Use the spoon card patterns with the "Stir Crazy"
Pocket Pal on page 56.

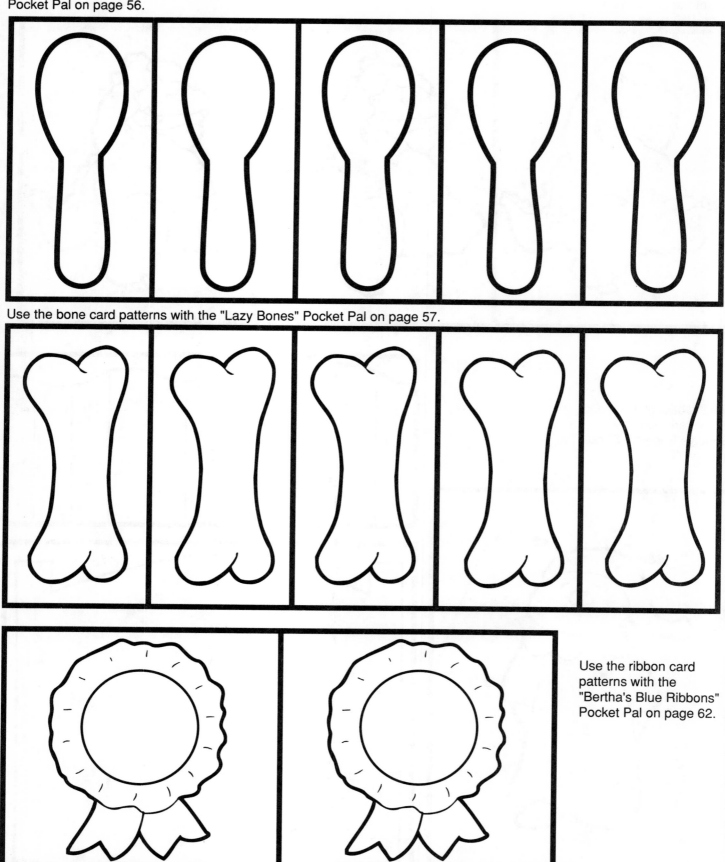

Use the bone card patterns with the "Lazy Bones" Pocket Pal on page 57.

Use the ribbon card
patterns with the
"Bertha's Blue Ribbons"
Pocket Pal on page 62.

Use the genie and bottle card patterns with the "Spin The Bottle" Pocket Pal on page 68.

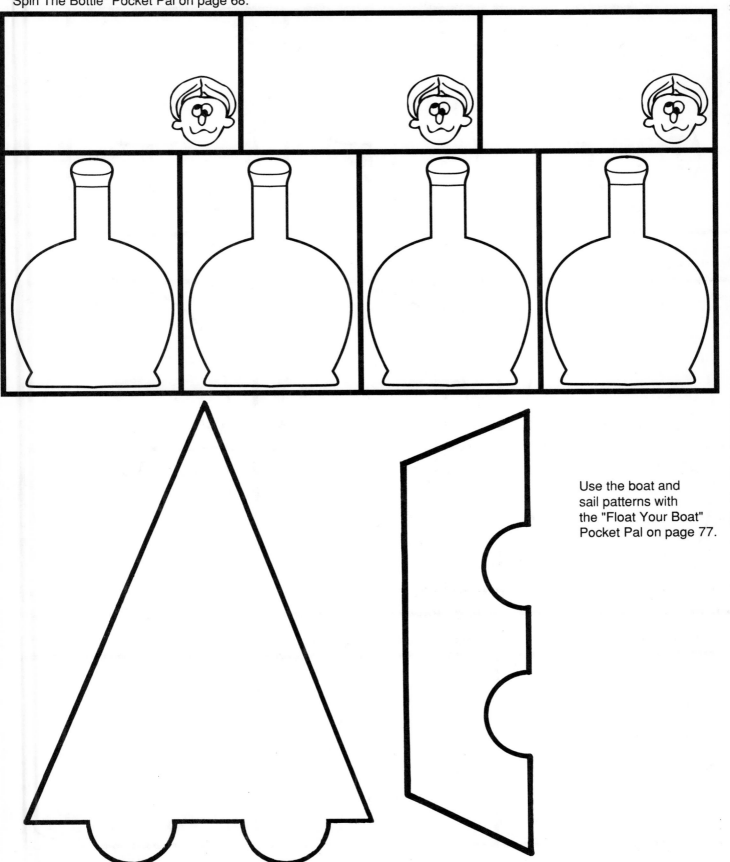

Use the boat and sail patterns with the "Float Your Boat" Pocket Pal on page 77.

Patterns

Use the coin card patterns with the "Davy Jones's Locker"
Pocket Pal on page 70.

Use the eggshell card patterns with the "Dinosaur Days" Pocket Pal on page 74.

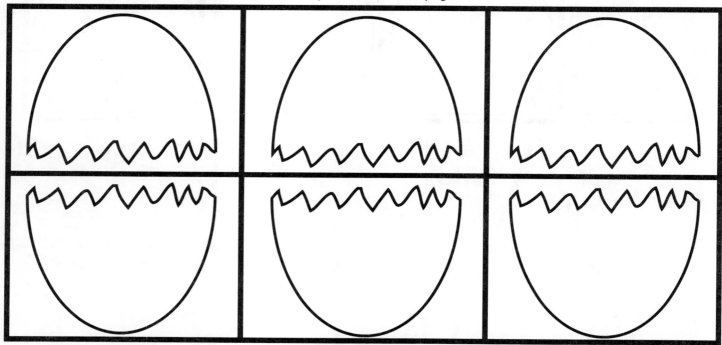

Use the teddy bear card patterns with the "The Bear Facts" Pocket Pal on page 81.

Use the cookie card patterns with the "Quack's Snack Attack" Clip-on on page 87, the "Monster Mouth" File Folder on page 105, and the "Animal Snackers" File Folder on page 124.

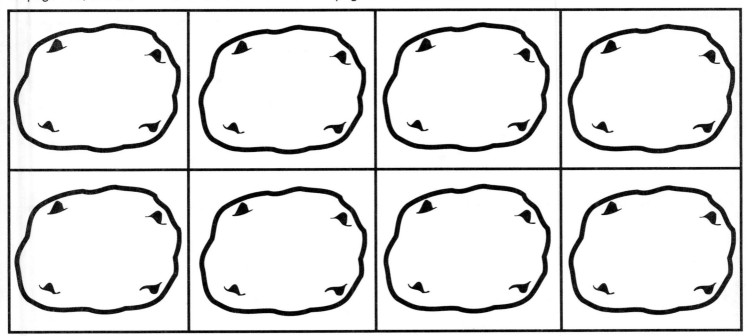

Use the clown card patterns with the "Clown Time" Clip-on on page 88.

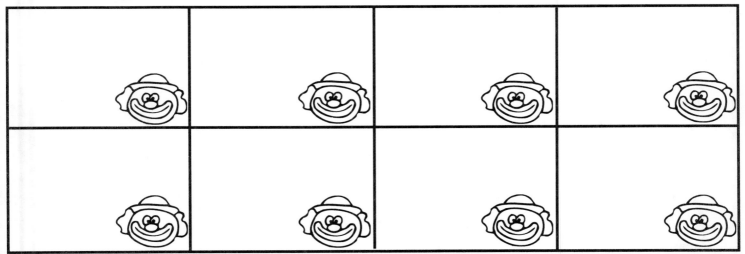

Use the pig card patterns with the "Cold Cash!" Clip-on on page 93.

Patterns

Use the seed card patterns with the "USS Seed" Clip-on on page 98.

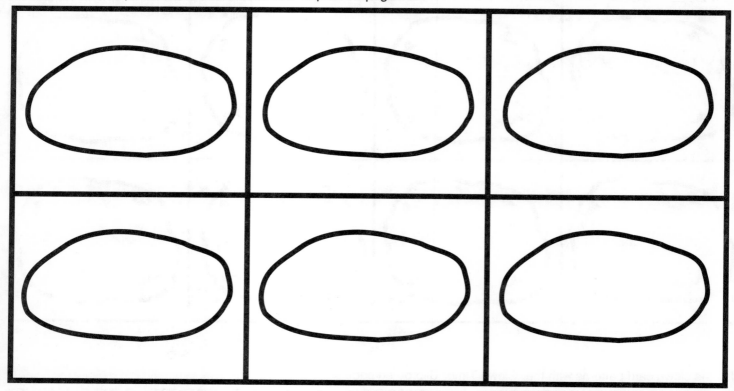

Use the bow card patterns with the "Pretty In Pink" File Folder on page 111.

Use the egg patterns with the "Ozzie Ostrich" File Folder on page 113.

Use the seashell patterns with the "Shell It Out!" File Folder on page 114.

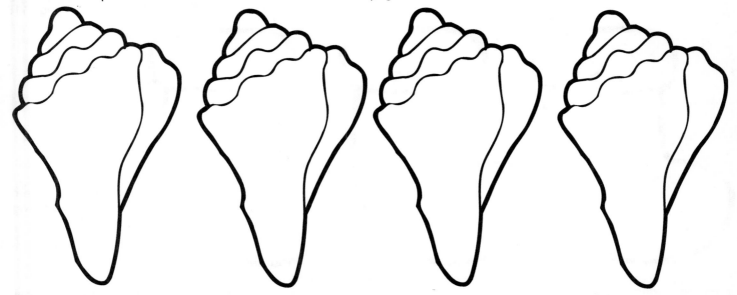

Use the baseball patterns with the "Dandy Doubleheader" File Folder on page 117 and the "Duck!" Skillboard on page 139.

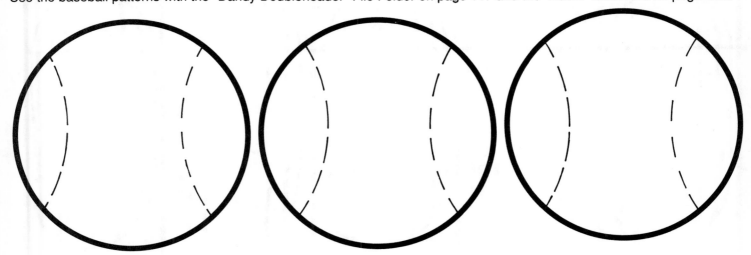

Patterns

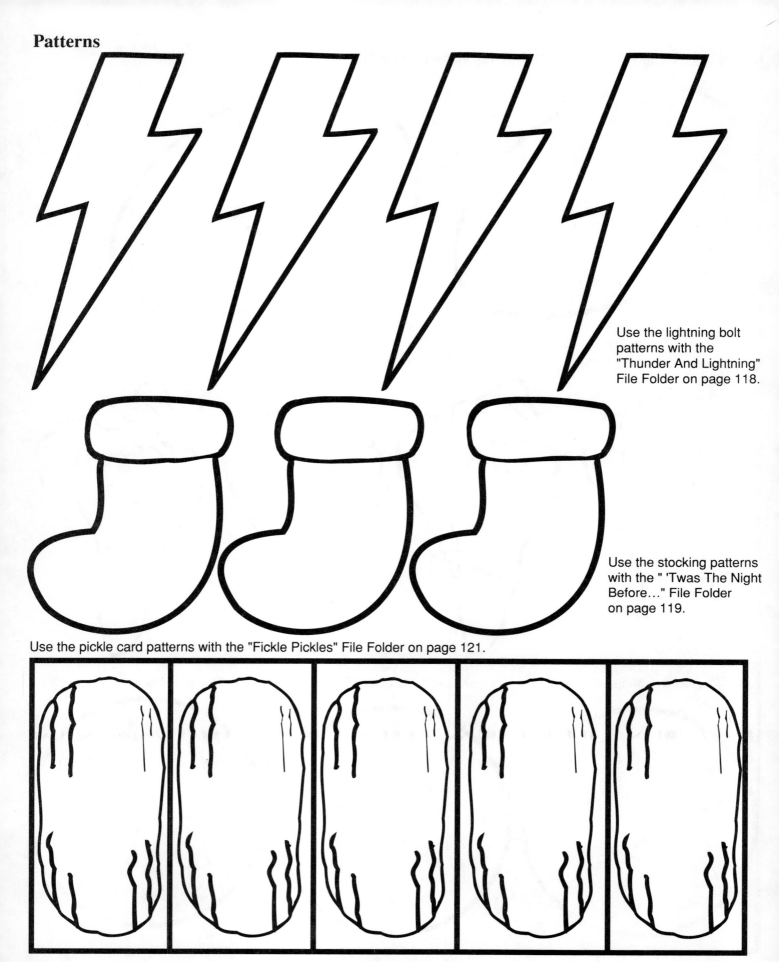

Use the lightning bolt patterns with the "Thunder And Lightning" File Folder on page 118.

Use the stocking patterns with the " 'Twas The Night Before…" File Folder on page 119.

Use the pickle card patterns with the "Fickle Pickles" File Folder on page 121.

Use the sheep patterns with the "Counting Sheep" File Folder
on page 123.

Use the bee patterns with the "Busy Math Bees" File Folder on page 126.

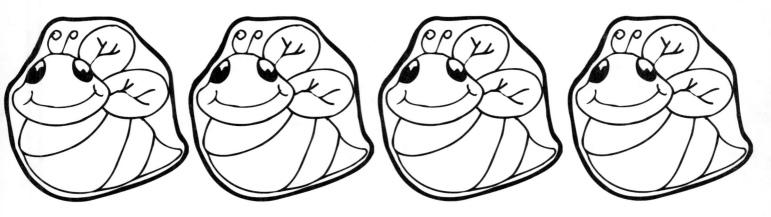

Use the mice card patterns with the "Pied Piper Parade" Skillboard on page 132.

Patterns

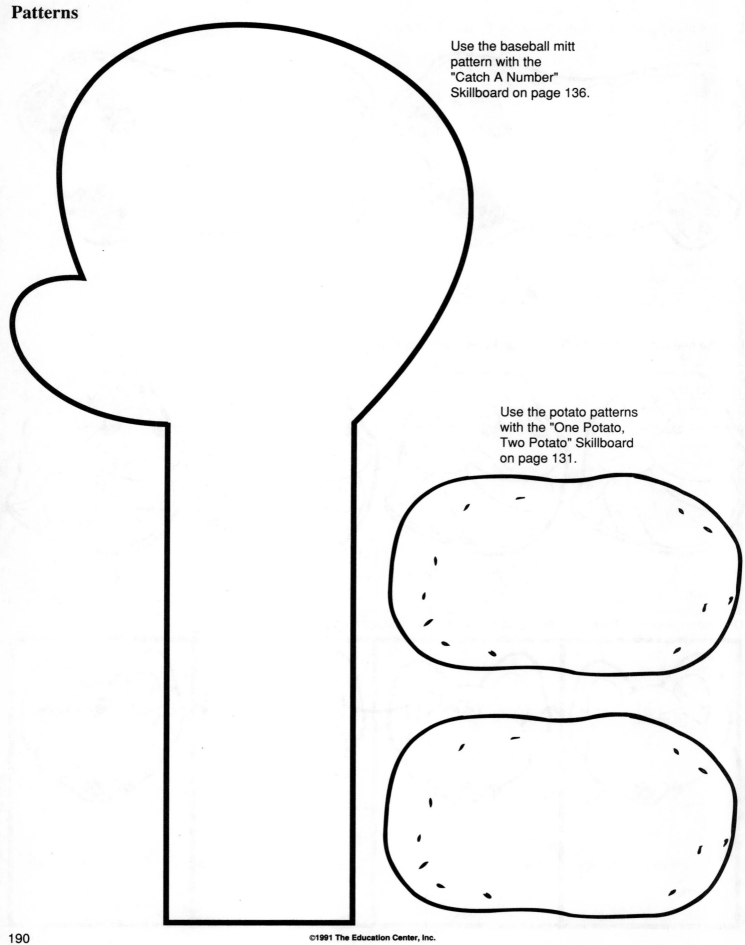

Use the baseball mitt
pattern with the
"Catch A Number"
Skillboard on page 136.

Use the potato patterns
with the "One Potato,
Two Potato" Skillboard
on page 131.

Use the bulb patterns with the "Night Lights" Skillboard
on page 143.

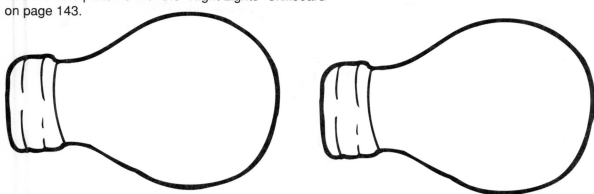

Use the pillow card patterns with the "Time To Wake Up" Skillboard on page 146.

Use the beach balls with the "Seymour Seal" Skillboard on page 151.

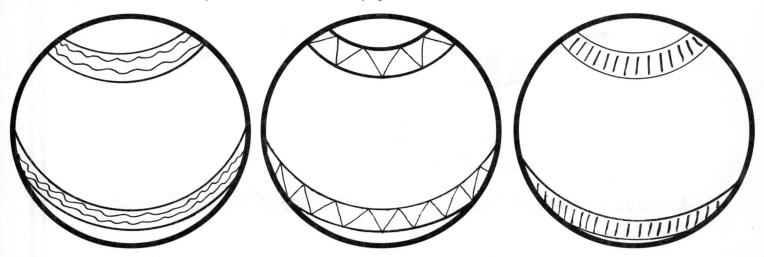

Patterns

Use the apple patterns with the "Bobbing For Apples" Skillboard on page 154.

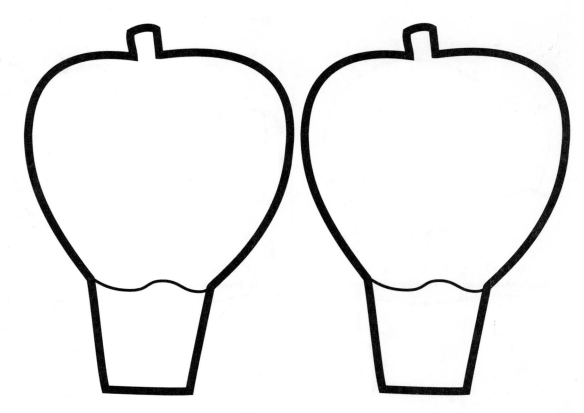

Use the puppy patterns with the "Bedtime For Polly's Puppies" Skillboard on page 155.

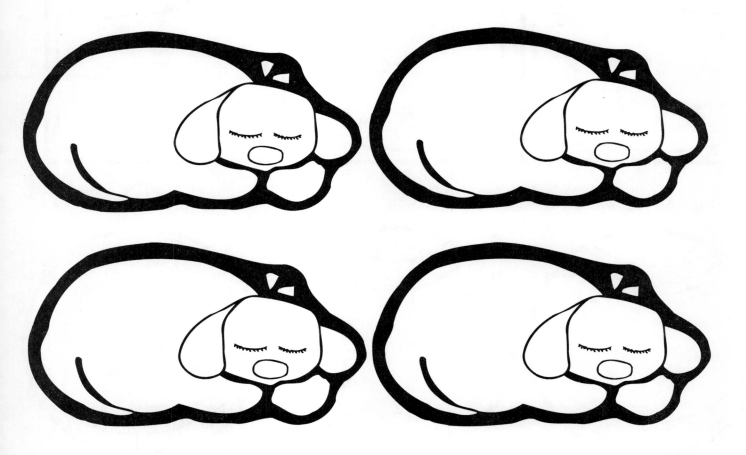